First ICARD Workshop 2023

Prague, Czech Republic
12 September 2023

ISBN: 978-1-7138-9032-4

Printed from e-media with permission by:

Curran Associates, Inc.
57 Morehouse Lane
Red Hook, NY 12571

CURRAN ASSOCIATES INC. proceedings.com

Some format issues inherent in the e-media version may also appear in this print version.

Association for Computational Linguistics
209 N. Eighth Street
Stroudsburg, Pennsylvania 18360

Phone: 1-570-476-8006
Fax: 1-570-476-0860

acl@aclweb.org

Additional copies of this publication are available from:

Curran Associates, Inc.
57 Morehouse Lane
Red Hook, NY 12571 USA
Phone: 845-758-0400
Fax: 845-758-2633
Email: curran@proceedings.com
Web: www.proceedings.com

TABLE OF CONTENTS

Global and local prosodic entrainment in a task-oriented interaction in autistic and neurotypical children

Joanna Kruyt
Institute of Informatics,
Slovak Academy of Sciences/
in Bratislava, Slovakia
FIIT, Slovak Technical University
in Bratislava, Slovakia
joanna.kruyt@savba.sk

Katarína Polónyiová and **Daniela Ostatníková**
Academic Research Center for Autism,
Institute of Physiology, Faculty of Medicine,
Comenius University in Bratislava, Slovakia

Štefan Beňuš
Institute of Informatics, Slovak Academy of Sciences in Bratislava, Slovakia/
Constantine the Philosopher University in Nitra, Slovakia

Abstract

Entrainment is an inherently interactive phenomenon whereby speakers tend to become more similar over time, for example in their way of speaking or prosody. Prosodic entrainment is associated with positive social measures. Autism spectrum disorder (ASD), on the other hand, is associated with social difficulties, as well as unusual prosody. Taken together, this could suggest that individuals with and without ASD show differences in prosodic entrainment. Such a between-group difference would be a promising direction for automatic, speech-based diagnostic screening tools. The present study aimed to characterise prosodic entrainment in Slovak children with and without ASD using several measurements, to understand participants' entrainment behaviour on multiple levels. Results paint a complex picture of prosodic entrainment in this corpus, but no significant between-group differences in prosodic entrainment were found using both local and global methods, suggesting that prosodic entrainment alone might not be the most promising direction for diagnostic screening tools.

1 Introduction

Early diagnosis of autism spectrum disorder (ASD) is crucial, as it allows for early intervention and can significantly improve quality of life for a child with ASD and their family (e.g. Elder et al., 2017; Fernell et al., 2013). However, getting a formal diagnosis is complicated: waiting lists for assessments are often long, and the process of testing a child and interviewing their family members is time-consuming and requires certified experts. While it is clear that automatic tests cannot replace a comprehensive ASD assessment needed to evaluate and support an individual on the spectrum, any tools that can be used to screen children or assist the diagnostic process could speed up the process and may be especially beneficial to groups that are underdiagnosed with ASD, such as girls (e.g. Gould and Ashton-Smith, 2011; Dean et al., 2017) or children of colour (e.g. Durkin et al., 2017).

Such screening tools can rely on different types of data, but a common way to investigate differences between verbal individuals with ASD and neurotypical peers is centered around speech and language. It must be noted that many tools to distinguish children with ASD from NT children based on language alone usually require the children to have reached a specific level of language development, which not all children with ASD reach. While prosodic entrainment may be determined on the basis of non-verbal vocalisations, this is not commonly done. The present paper will focus on verbal children with ASD.

Existing research has shown that individuals with ASD can be distinguished from individuals without ASD based on their speech: for example, Parish-Morris et al. (2016) correctly identified 68% of children with ASD and 100% of neurotypical (NT) children from a group of children with ASD, children with other (developmental) disorders, and NT children based on their acoustic features and word choices. Acoustic-prosodic features such as speech rate and fundamental frequency (f0) facilitated the distinction between the three groups. Similarly, other studies have used combinations of acoustic features and various machine learning algorithms to distinguish between children with ASD, their NT peers, and children with different developmental disorders (e.g. Lee et al., 2013; Deng et al., 2017-07). In other words, it appears that children with ASD can be distinguished from children

Proceedings of the First ICARD Workshop, pages 1–11
September 12, 2023

without ASD or those with other developmental disorders based on their speech and language.

A specific phenomenon that is inherently interactive, only occurs during conversation, and can be observed in language is *entrainment* (other terms are also used, such as *alignment*, *convergence*, and *synchrony*) and describes the phenomenon of increased similarity between two interacting people. Entrainment can occur in multiple modalities, such as facial expressions, body movement, and language, and this paper will focus on the latter. Some evidence suggests that individuals with ASD may exhibit or use entrainment differently than NT individuals, specifically at the prosodic level. For example, according to previous research, the prosody of individuals with ASD is often perceived as unusual or "odd", and their pitch can be perceived as unusually flat or overly varied (e.g. Paul et al., 2009; Nadig and Shaw, 2012). Even in the gold standard of ASD diagnostics, the Autism Diagnostic Observation Schedule (ADOS), speech and prosody play a role: for example, inappropriately fast or slow speech, "odd" intonation, unusual pitch and stress, and flat or monotone speech are included as characteristics of ASD (Lord et al., 2008).

These observations may suggest different linguistic entrainment patterns in individuals with ASD, compared to NT individuals. Moreover, linguistic entrainment, specifically at the prosodic level, has been associated with positive social measures such as feelings of closeness and interpersonal rapport (e.g. Michalsky et al., 2018; Pardo et al., 2012; Chartrand and Bargh, 1999). ASD, on the other hand, is associated with marked social difficulties: individuals with ASD report struggling with friendships and romantic relationships more than their NT peers (e.g. Bossaert et al., 2015; Taheri et al., 2016). A possible between-group difference in prosodic entrainment behaviour could in part explain these seemingly unrelated traits.

Further evidence for possible differences in linguistic entrainment between NT and ASD populations comes from research that suggests that individuals with ASD exhibit lower degrees of synchrony or entrainment in other modalities, such as body swaying rhythm (Marsh et al., 2013), pendulum swinging (Fitzpatrick et al., 2018), and finger tapping (Koehne et al., 2016). Reduced entrainment can also be observed in conversational settings: for example, compared to their NT peers, individuals with ASD exhibit less entrainment to their conversational partners in terms of head and hand movements (Noel et al., 2017) and eye blinking patterns (Nakano et al., 2011).

The present paper aims to investigate whether prosodic entrainment differs between verbal children with ASD and their neurotypical peers. Since entrainment is an inherently interactive phenomenon that is associated with positive social measures, a between-group difference in this behaviour is promising for the development of automatic, speech-based diagnostic screening tools. First, prior work on entrainment in these groups will be reviewed.

2 Related work

When it comes to prosodic entrainment in individuals with ASD, a handful of studies have been conducted (see Kruyt and Beňuš (2021) for a review). For example, Ochi et al. (2019) used the "time aligned moving average" method (TAMA by Kousidis et al. (2008), which involves extracting features from a moving window and cross-correlating the resulting time series, to assess entrainment during the diagnostic interview of an ADOS module (Lord et al., 2008). Ochi et al. (2019) reported a range of findings that, taken together, suggest that there may be reduced entrainment in adults with ASD (with a mean age of 26.9 years) compared to their NT peers (mean age of 29.6 years), though it is important to note that all participants in their study were male. While it is common for males to be overrepresented in ASD research (Watkins et al., 2014), the absence of female participants in this study begs the question of whether its results are generalisable to the wider population with ASD.

Lehnert-LeHouillier et al. (2020) elicited task-oriented conversation from participants with (mean age of 12.2 years) and without ASD (mean age of 12.1 years) during a collaborative task and used a geometric approach to quantify entrainment on mean fundamental frequency (f0) and f0 range features by comparing the difference between speakers in the first and last third of every interaction. Results showed that entrainment was observed in conversations with NT participants, but dis-entrainment was measured in conversations with participants with ASD. There was a significant difference between groups on mean f0 contribution: "on average, participants with ASD contributed 71% less to the convergence in mean f0 during the conversation compared to their NT peers" (Lehnert-

LeHouillier et al., 2020), p. 8). Importantly, results also suggested experimenter's entrainment behaviour differed based on participants: there was a significant interaction effect between age and diagnosis (i.e. ASD or NT) on the experimenter's contribution to the overall observed entrainment, suggesting that age and diagnosis influenced how the experimenter entrained to the participants and that some of the significant between-group differences in entrainment actually originated from the experimenters, rather than the participants.

A comprehensive investigation into entrainment in individuals with (mean age of 19.5 years) and without ASD (mean age of 15.5 years) and their first-degree relatives was conducted by Patel et al. (2022), who found between-group differences in prosodic entrainment: individuals with ASD showed a stronger tendency to dis-entrain rather than entrain, while the opposite was observed in their NT peers. Interestingly, this pattern was mirrored in the parental groups: parents of individuals with ASD (mean age of 50.1 years) also showed prosodic dis-entrainment compared to parents of NT participants (mean age of 47.0 years).

In general, research into prosodic entrainment in individuals with and without ASD is scarce, but results suggest that there may be a pattern of reduced prosodic entrainment in individuals with ASD. However,in each study, different operationalisations and methods are used to measure entrainment: some studies investigated entrainment in smaller time-frames, while others measured it over whole conversations. Similarly, not all studies took into account who was entraining to whom.

In the present study, we will use several previously methods to measure prosodic entrainment, in order to investigate it in different time-frames (i.e. both locally and globally) within the same corpus. Additionally, the age group of our participants differs from the age of participants in existing studies: participants in prior studies were either adults, or slightly older children, and the participants in our study are younger. Comparing the results from our study to those of prior research may shed some light on the development of entrainment behaviours over time.

3 Methods

3.1 Participants and procedure

We collaborated with the Academic Research Center for Autism (ARCA) in Bratislava, Slovakia, and recruited two groups of participants: children with (suspected) ASD (diagnosis was later confirmed with standardised diagnostic tests) and neurotypical (NT) children without suspected ASD or other developmental disorders. All children were native speakers of Slovak and had normal to corrected sight and hearing.

In total, we recruited 67 children (14F, 62M), 41 of which were diagnosed with ASD (7F, 34F) and 35 of which were neurotypical (7F, 28M). The mean age of all recruited children was 9.21 (±1.86) years. For more details on the demographics and test scores of the recruited participants, see Table 1. Note that not all data was included in every analysis due to technical issues.

Table 1: Summary of demographic information and test scores for both groups of participants.

	ASD (7F, 34M		NT (7F, 28M)		t-test
	mean (sd)	range	mean (sd)	range	p
age	9.10 (1.71)	6.14 - 12.30	9.34 (2.04)	6.18 - 12.97	>0.05
IQ	96.80 (16.81)	52 - 131	105.8 (14.84)	67 - 134	<0.05
BRIEF	67.32 (9.61)	47 - 85	58.77 (12.81)	36 - 83	<0.01
ToM	8.29 (2.14)	2 - 14	12.17 (1.74)	8 - 15	<0.001

All children with suspected ASD underwent the full diagnostic procedure, consisting of the Autism Diagnostic Observation Schedule (ADOS) (Lord et al., 2008) and Autism Diagnostic Interview (Revised, ADI-R). Additionally, the Woodcock-Johnson test was administered to all children to obtain a measure of their intelligence quotient (IQ), and the Comic strip task (Cornish et al., 2010) was used to obtain a theory of mind (ToM) score for each child, since the role of ToM in entrainment is considered a topic of debate. Information regarding the executive functions (EF) of each child was collected using the Behavior Rating Inventory of Executive Function (BRIEF) questionnaire (Gioia et al., 2000) that was filled out by the children's parent(s)/caregiver(s), since executive functioning may also play a role in entrainment. The Slovak versions of all materials were used and all tasks were administered and scored by a certified psychologist.

3.2 Maps task

To elicit conversation, we asked participants to complete the Maps task. In this collaborative task, two participants are given maps that differ slightly. One participant's map has a pre-drawn route, that this participant has to try and describe to their fellow player. This "instruction follower" has to try and replicate the "instruction giver"'s route as precisely as possible on their own map. The Maps task is commonly used to elicit task-oriented dialogue.

The experimenter who participated in the Maps task with each child was the same clinician who administered the other tests, to ensure that the child was familiar and comfortable with them. The experimenter was thus aware of whether the child received an ASD diagnosis or not. To eliminate the influence of any experimenter bias, she received detailed instructions prior to the experiment. She was aware of the purpose of the study, but primarily knew about a lexical entrainment analysis and knew little about the prosodic analyses.

Typically during a Maps task, roles switch between trials. However, such constant rule-changing can be challenging for individuals with executive functioning difficulties such as many children with ASD. For this reason, we only included one role switch in the Maps task: during the first 3 trials (1 practice trial of which data was not analysed, 2 "real" trials), the child followed instructions, while during the last 3 trials (1 practice, 2 "real"), the child gave instructions.

3.3 Audio recordings and pre-processing

To minimise distress in the children with ASD who often have sensory issues, a directional tabletop microphone and Lavalier microphone were used rather than head-mounted microphones. For reasons of consistency, the experimenter was also recorded with a directional tabletop microphone. Audio recordings were annotated by experience annotators who are native Slovak speakers. Recordings were orthographically transcribed using Transcriber before being transformed to Praat TextGrids that were used to manually convert Transcriber's utterances into IPUs (inter-pausal units) with a silence threshold of 250ms by two trained annotators who were two native speakers of Slovak.

3.4 Analyses

We excluded three files because of technical and audio quality issues, so in total, we used 73 audio files. For each speaker, we used the manually aligned TextGrids to extract median f0 per IPU from the corresponding recordings. We implemented a two-pass filter to avoid pitch tracking errors (Looze and Rauzy, 2009) and used speaker-dependent pitch floors and ceilings: 100–450 Hz for children (Pedersen et al., 2015), and 75-500 for the adult, female experimenter.

3.4.1 Global prosodic entrainment

We used a method introduced by Lehnert-LeHouillier et al. (2020) to measure global prosodic entrainment (see Figure 1), as this allows for the investigation of directionality of entrainment, i.e. how much each speaker entrained to the other speaker. Based on the findings by Lehnert-LeHouillier et al. (2020), who found that the experimenter entrained differently to participants with and without ASD, this was deemed the most appropriate method to analyse our data.

Following Lehnert-LeHouillier et al. (2020), we drew two points that each represented a speaker's median f0 at the start ("first third" in Figure 1) and end of the conversation ("last third" in Figure 1). Next, a "matching line" was drawn to represent the scenario in which both speakers' features are identical. The difference in distance from the start point to this matching line (d1) and the distance from the end point to the matching line (d2) is an indication of the overall entrainment. To calculate each speaker's individual contribution to the overall entrainment, the proportion of change along both the x-axis (speaker B) and the y-axis (speaker A) can be calculated.

Figure 1: Visual representation of the geometric method by Lehnert-LeHouillier et al. (2020), explained in more detail in Section 3.4.1. This figure is inspired by the figure in Lehnert-LeHouillier et al. (2020).

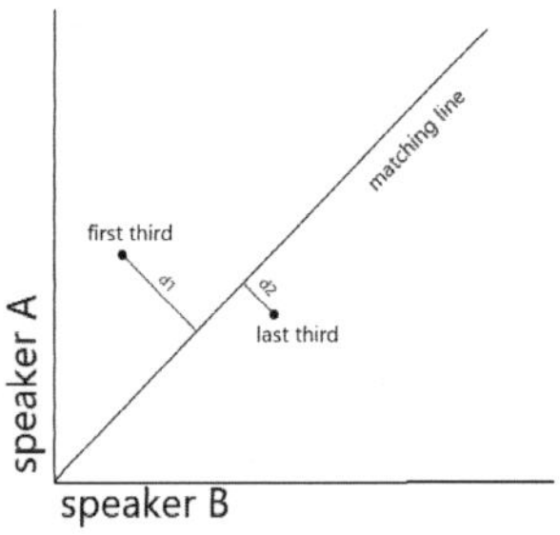

Rather than extracting features from the first and last third of an interaction, as was done by Lehnert-LeHouillier et al. (2020), we calculated median f0 (extracted per IPU and then averaged weighted by IPU duration) for the first two trials and the last two trials of our Maps task. It is important to note that between these trials, the task roles of the participants switched (i.e. the child acted as the instruction follower during the first two trials, and as the instruction giver during the last two trials). The trial/role variable thus represents both a difference in roles as well as in elapsed time.

We investigated whether the overall observed entrainment was predicted by various variables using the following linear mixed effects model formula:

entrainment $\sim$ group * trial/role + ToM + gender + age + BRIEF + IQ + (1 | participant)

A group * trial/role interaction effect was included since we hypothesised that task role (i.e. instruction giver vs follower) may influence entrainment, and roles in our Maps task switched halfway through. We included the interaction effect to account for the possibility that children from different group react differently to the different roles.

Because prior research by Lehnert-LeHouillier et al. (2020) suggests that differences in observed entrainment between groups may in fact be due to differences in how the adult experimenter interacts with the children, we constructed an additional model using the following formula:

entrainment contribution experimenter $\sim$ group * trial/role + ToM + gender + age + (1 | participant).

BRIEF and IQ score were not included in this model as we assumed that these factors are not salient or explicit enough to warrant any changes in behaviour of an interlocutor, but the experimenter was aware of the child's diagnosis and their ToM score (as this related to her own research goals as a separate part of this project), so ToM score was kept in the formula. All the LMEMs were implemented using the R package lme4 (Bates et al., 2014) and significance of effects was assessed using lmerTest (Kuznetsova et al., 2017).

3.4.2 Local prosodic entrainment

Additionally, we investigated prosodic entrainment at the local level: we measured proximity, convergence, and synchrony following Levitan et al. (2011-06). This was done to ensure that prosodic entrainment was investigated comprehensively.

Local proximity was determined by using a paired t-test to compare the difference between a target IPU and its adjacent IPU uttered by the other speaker, to the mean difference between the target IPU and 10 random non-adjacent IPUs by the other speaker. Local convergence is calculated conducting a Pearson correlation on the difference between a target IPU and its adjacent IPU uttered by the other speaker, and IPU number as an indication of elapsed time. Local synchrony is measured by performing a Pearson correlation on a target IPU and its adjacent IPU uttered by the other speaker. For local convergence and local synchrony, Pearson correlations are repeated 10x on randomly shuffled data and significant results are only considered valid if less than 2 of these randomly shuffled correlations return significant results.

Note that in the analysis conducted in this experiment, we used speaker-based z-score norming rather than gender-based z-score norming as was used by Levitan et al. (2011-06).

4 Results

4.1 Global prosodic entrainment

The intercept of the model used to predict overall observed prosodic entrainment, at which values correspond to group = NT, trial/role = last two trials, theory of mind score = 0, gender = M, age = 0, IQ = 0, and BRIEF score = 0, is estimated to be 0.91 (see Table 2).

Table 2: Effects in the LMEM constructed for the overall observed prosodic entrainment analysis. No effects were found to be significant.

effect	beta	std	t	df	p
intercept	0.91	9.17	0.10	136	0.922
group	-2.87	2.68	-1.07	136	0.287
trial/role	-2.14	2.11	-1.01	136	0.314
group*trial/role	1.97	3.11	0.63	136	0.528
ToM	0.03	0.42	0.07	136	0.943
gender	-1.59	2.01	-0.79	136	0.430
age	0.18	0.43	0.42	136	0.677
BRIEF	0.02	0.01	0.34	136	0.732
IQ	-0.01	0.05	-0.28	136	0.782

Within this model, all effects were found to be non-significant. Non-significant, negative effects were group, trial/role, gender, and IQ. Non-significant, positive effects were ToM and BRIEF score, age, and the interaction between trial and group (see Table 2).

To investigate whether the adult entrained differently to children from either group or during different trial/roles, an additional LMEM was constructed. In this model, the intercept, which corresponds to values of group = NT, trial/role = last two trials, ToM and age, are 0, and gender = M, was estimated to be 0.23 (see Table 3).

In this model, most effects were positive and non-significant, such as group, ToM score, and age. Effects that were negative and non-significant were gender and the interaction between group and trial/role (see Table 3). A significant positive effect

Table 3: Effects in the LMEM constructed for the experimenter's contribution to the overall observed prosodic entrainment analysis. Significant effects are indicated with an asterisk.

effect	beta	std	t	df	p
intercept	0.23	0.16	1.44	138	0.151
group	0.05	0.08	0.55	138	0.581
trial/role	0.18	0.06	2.74	138	0.007*
group*trial/role	-0.14	0.09	-1.45	138	0.151
ToM	0.01	0.01	0.47	138	0.638
gender	-0.05	0.06	-0.87	138	0.386
age	0.02	0.01	1.46	138	0.147

Figure 2: Plot of the experimenter's relative contribution to the overall observed entrainment during different trial/role (trial12 represents the first two real, non-practice trials while trial34 represents the last two trials) and to children from different groups.

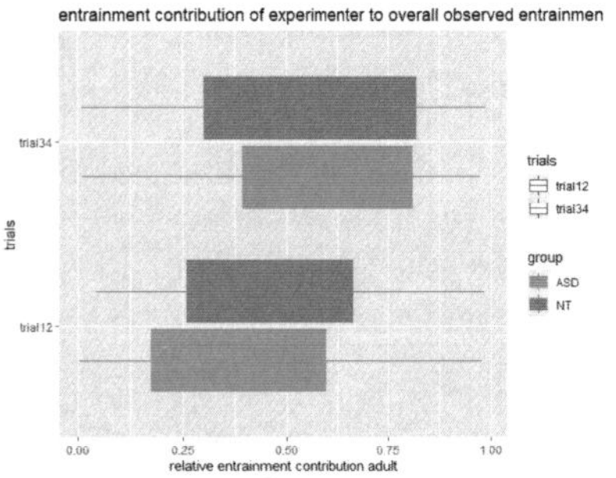

of trial/role was found, suggesting that in the second two trials, the experimenter contributed significantly more to the overall entrainment than during the first two trials, and that this happened irrespective of the group membership of the child. This is shown in Figure 2, which suggests that that the experimenter entrained similarly to children with and without ASD regardless of the trial.

4.2 Local prosodic entrainment

An additional set of analyses was conducted to measure entrainment on a different time-scale, namely the local one. Local proximity, convergence, and synchrony were measured, and only a limited number of conversations returned a significant result.

In terms of local proximity, the number of significant measurements of entrainment (N=0) and dis-entrainment (N=1) were equal for the NT and ASD group (see Table 4). A similar finding was obtained for local synchrony, where significant entrainment was not found, and significant dis-entrainment was found in 4 conversations in the NT group, and in 5 conversations in the ASD group (see Table 5).

Table 4: Summary of results for the local proximity measurements. Numbers in cells reflect the number of conversations that returned significant findings.

	sig. entr.	sig. dis.	total sig.	conv.
ASD	0	1	1	39
NT	0	1	1	34
total	0	2	2	73

Table 5: Summary of results for the local synchrony measurements. Numbers in cells reflect the number of conversations (conv.) that returned significant entrainment (sig. entr.) or dis-entrainment (sig. dis.).

	sig. entr.	sig. dis.	total sig.	conv.
ASD	0	5	5	39
NT	0	4	4	34
total	0	9	9	73

The measurement of local entrainment that showed the most substantial between-group differences was local convergence. Using this measurement, significant entrainment was found in 2 conversations in the NT group, and 0 in the ASD group. Note that this is the only local prosodic entrainment measurement that produced significant entrainment results. Moreover, significant dis-entrainment was measured in 7 conversations in the ASD group, and in 4 interactions in the NT group (see Table 6). While this could be taken as an indication of reduced prosodic entrainment and increased prosodic dis-entrainment in the ASD group compared to the NT group, we believe that the fact that the difference between groups is so small, and was only observed on 1 out of 4 measurements, does not indicate substantial, systematic differences between groups when it comes to prosodic entrainment.

Table 6: Summary of results for the local convergence measurements. Numbers in cells reflect the number of conversations that returned significant findings.

	sig. entr.	sig. dis	total sig.	conv.
ASD	0	7	7	39
NT	2	4	6	34
total	2	11	13	73

In short, the tables illustrate that between-group differences are absent or minimal, and while we cannot say with certainty that there is no statistically significant difference between groups in terms of local prosodic entrainment, we have sufficient evidence to believe that the two groups do not consistently and systematically differ in this behaviour.

Interestingly, dyads who showed significant (dis-)entrainment according to one of the local mea-

Table 7: Dyad IDs of the dyads that showed significant entrainment (sig. entr.) or significant dis-entrainment (sig. dis.) according to the three different measures of local entrainment.

proximity				convergence				synchrony			
sig. entr.		sig. dis.		sig. entr.		sig. dis.		sig. entr.		sig. dis.	
ASD	NT	ASD	NT	ASD	NT	ASD	NT	ASD	NT	ASD	NT
		A22	K23		K12	A06	K14			A06	K17
					K17	A16	K16			A08	K26
						A17	K23			A09	K28
						A20	K27			A22	K30
						A21				A41	
						A37					
						A38					

sures of entrainment, often did not show entrainment according to a different measure. Table 7 shows that some dyads, such as A06, A22, and K23, exhibit significant dis-entrainment on more than one dimension. However, for the majority of dyads, this is not the case: most dyads show no significant (dis-)entrainment at all, and out of those that do, most dyads show significant (dis-)entrainment on one measure and exhibit no significant (dis-)entrainment on the other dimensions. In other words, there seems to be no clear pattern in the entrainment patterns of individual dyads.

5 Discussion

The two groups in this experiment did not differ significantly in terms of age. The groups did differ significantly on IQ score, as well as ToM score and BRIEF score (see Table 1). Although we tried to match our NT participants to the children with ASD that we recruited on age and approximate IQ, it is difficult to match two groups of participants perfectly. Our NT group ended up having a significantly higher mean IQ than our group with ASD. Additionally, our NT group performed significantly better on the ToM test. This is in line with findings that suggest that children with ASD may have ToM impairments (e.g. Baron-Cohen, 2000; Baron-Cohen et al., 1985; Tager-Flusberg, 2007).

The same applies to the executive functioning assessment as measured by the BRIEF questionnaire: the NT group had a significantly lower score than the group with ASD, which reflects fewer issues with executive functioning in day-to-day life. Again, this is in line with previous research that shows that ASD is associated with executive functioning challenges (Demetriou et al., 2018).

5.1 Global prosodic entrainment

The results of the geometric prosodic entrainment analysis suggest that group, ToM score, gender, age, trial/role, IQ score, and BRIEF score do not significantly predict the degree of prosodic entrainment that was measured between a child and an experimenter during a Maps task.

Most prior research into prosodic entrainment in individuals with and without ASD suggests that it differs significantly between groups, and often is reduced in the group with ASD. However, in many of these studies, different methods are used to measure entrainment, and most of these methods do not measure each individual's contribution to the overall observed entrainment. A study that shows why this is essential was conducted by Lehnert-LeHouillier et al. (2020), who found a difference between groups in overall observed entrainment, but then found that some of this difference could be explained by the experimenter's behaviour rather than that of the child. While our results neither suggest a significant difference in overall entrainment between groups, nor a significant effects of any predictors on the degree of prosodic entrainment, we nonetheless aimed to investigate whether the experimenter's behaviour towards children from the two groups differed, especially since the experimenter was not naive to the diagnosis of the children she interacted with. For this reason, we constructed an additional statistical model and plotted the experimenter's contribution to the overall observed entrainment in Figure 2, and both suggest that the experimenter entrained similarly to children with and without ASD, which is not in line with findings by Lehnert-LeHouillier et al. (2020).

A possible difference between the experimenter in the present study and in that conducted by Lehnert-LeHouillier et al. (2020) could be their awareness of the children's diagnosis. While the experimenter in our study knew whether a child she was interacting with was diagnosed with ASD or not, we provided her with training in hopes of ensuring that she behaved the same towards all children. It is unclear whether the experimenter(s) in the Lehnert-LeHouillier et al. (2020) study were naive to the children's diagnosis or not, and whether they received training prior to the experiment. This could perhaps, at least in part, explain the differences between the findings of both studies.

5.2 Local prosodic entrainment

An additional set of analyses was conducted to measure entrainment on a different time-scale, namely the local one. Local proximity, convergence, and synchrony were measured, and only a limited number of conversations returned a significant result.

In terms of local proximity, the number of significant measurements of entrainment (N=0) and dis-entrainment (N=1) were equal for the NT and ASD group (see Table 4). A similar finding was obtained for local synchrony, where significant entrainment was not found, and significant dis-entrainment was found in 4 conversations in the NT group, and in 5 conversations in the NT group (see Table 5).

The measurement of local entrainment that showed the most substantial between-group differences was local convergence. Using this measurement, significant entrainment was found in 2 conversations in the NT group, and 0 in the ASD group. Note that this is the only local prosodic entrainment measurement that produced significant entrainment results. Moreover, significant dis-entrainment was measured in 7 conversations in the ASD group, and in 4 interactions in the NT group (see Table 6). While this could be taken as an indication of reduced prosodic entrainment and increased prosodic dis-entrainment in the ASD group compared to the NT group, we believe that the fact that the difference between groups is so small, and was only observed on 1 out of 4 measurements, does not indicate substantial, systematic differences between groups when it comes to prosodic entrainment.

In short, the tables illustrate that between-group differences are either absent or minimal, and while we cannot say with certainty that there is no statistically significant difference between groups in terms of local prosodic entrainment, we have sufficient evidence to believe that the two groups do not consistently differ in this behaviour.

Interestingly, dyads who showed significant (dis-)entrainment according to one of the local measures of entrainment, often did not show entrainment according to a different measure. Table 7 shows that some dyads, such as A06, A22, and K23, exhibit significant dis-entrainment on more than one dimension. However, for the majority of dyads, this is not the case: most dyads show no significant (dis-)entrainment at all, and out of those that do, most dyads show significant (dis-)entrainment on one measure and exhibit no significant (dis-)entrainment on the other dimensions. In other words, there seems to be no clear pattern in the entrainment patterns of individual dyads.

5.3 General discussion

The results of our global entrainment analyses are not in line with those of Lehnert-LeHouillier et al. (2020) and suggest no significant differences between groups in terms of entrainment or entrainment contribution. Similarly, no consistent differences between groups can be found in any of the local entrainment measurements, despite previous studies suggesting a somewhat consistent pattern of reduced prosodic entrainment in individuals with ASD compared to individuals without ASD. It is possible that this pattern of reduced entrainment only emerges at an older age: almost all participants in previous studies were older than our participants by at least a few years.

We did include age as a fixed effect in our models and found that it did not significantly predict entrainment. It is possible that age alone does not predict entrainment, but that the interaction between age and group membership (i.e. ASD or NT) influences entrainment behaviour: plausibly, as a child grows older, the social interactions they participate in become more complex, which could require more cognitive resources especially for children with ASD who may struggle to navigate some social situations. Increased cognitive effort or load has been associated with decreased entrainment (Abel and Babel, 2017). Future research may aim to investigate how the social skills and abilities of children with and without ASD relate to their entrainment behaviours at different ages.

6 Conclusions

The aim of this study was to investigate prosodic entrainment in children with and without ASD on both the global and local level during the same task. The results of this study paint a complex picture of prosodic entrainment that does not seem to differ systematically between groups of children with or without ASD. More research about prosodic entrainment, its underlying psychological mechanisms, and possible social functions may further elucidate its potential as a screening tool, but at present, empirical evidence is insufficient to develop prosodic entrainment-based screening tools. It is possible that entrainment in other domains, such as body movement, offers a more promising target for easily implementable screening tests, though the role of interaction in such forms of entrainment requires further investigation.

Limitations

Some important limitations of this study relate to experimental design choices we made considering the specific needs of children with ASD. For example, there was a switch in role halfway through the task. While we had good reasons for making this decision, it nonetheless means that task role and elapsed time are always conflated in our analyses (in our trial/role variable). Both of these factors have been shown to influence entrainment (e.g. Reichel et al., 2018), and it is possible that the effects of both cancelled each other out and contributed to the lack of significant results we observed.

The fact that our experimenter was also the clinician who administered other tests to the children similarly may have influenced our results: while we chose to ensure that the children were comfortable with the experimenter to minimise their anxiety and discomfort, the fact that the children were already familiar with the adult may have changed their behaviour towards her. If entrainment is related to social affiliation and rapport building, perhaps our participants felt that enough rapport had been built, and entrainment was no longer necessary. In general, the familiarity between participant and experimenter may make the results of our study more difficult to compare to existing studies.

Finally, we conducted our recordings in the same room where other tests were administered, despite the fact that this room is relatively loud and has an echo. Again, this was done to minimise any distress caused by unfamiliar environments in the children, especially those with ASD.

Another limitation of our study is that only entrainment on median f0 was considered, and no other features such as for example f0 range or speech rate were extracted. While additional analyses can and will be conducted on our collected corpus, it is also important to mention that the recording quality does not allow for the reliable extraction of all features. For example, because we used directional table top microphones rather than head-mounted microphones (again, to minimise distress in children with ASD who often have sensory sensitivities), it is difficult to extract reliable intensity values. Nonetheless, we believe that our collected corpus will be a valuable resource for future research.

Ethics Statement

Ethical approval for both the present experiment as well as the larger overarching research project that this study was part of, was obtained from ARCA's ethics board. Informed consent was obtained from parent(s)/caregiver(s) prior to the experiment. Participants and their parent(s)/caregiver(s) were compensated for their time and participation with gift vouchers.

It is important to note that caution must be taken surrounding the assumption of ToM or social impairments in disorders such as ASD: while traditionally, ASD has been associated with ToM impairments and inherent social deficits, recent empirical evidence suggests that this may be an incorrect assumption (e.g. Paynter et al., 2016; Gernsbacher and Yergeau, 2019). Rather than viewing the communication and ToM and social difficulties of individuals with ASD as their inherent deficits, difficulties with communication and "mind-reading" may be the result of "neurotype mismatches" that occur when an individual with ASD interacts with an NT individual. Individuals with ASD may not lack a theory of mind per se, but rather may struggle to understand the NT mind, specifically. Importantly, this works both ways: NT individuals seem to lack a theory of "autistic" mind (Sheppard et al., 2016; Heasman and Gillespie, 2018). This view is referred to as the "double empathy problem" (Milton, 2012) and is often advocated for by individuals with ASD. It is essential to keep this perspective in mind, especially considering the fact that most existing research into conversation coordination strategies of individuals with ASD was conducted on interactions with a neurotype mismatch.

Acknowledgements

We would like to thank all participants and their parent(s)/caregiver(s) for participating in this study. This project has received funding from the European Union's Horizon 2020 research and innovation programme under the Marie Skłodowska-Curie grant agreement No 859588, from the Slovak Granting Agency grant VEGA 2/0165/21, and the Slovak Research and Development Agency grant numbers APVV-21-0373 and APVV-20-0070.

References

Jennifer Abel and Molly Babel. 2017. Cognitive load reduces perceived linguistic convergence between dyads. *Language and Speech*, 60(3):479–502.

S. Baron-Cohen. 2000. Theory of mind and autism: A review. *International review of research in mental retardation*, 23:169–184.

S. Baron-Cohen, A.M. Leslie, and U. Frith. 1985. Does the autistic child have a "theory of mind"? *Cognition*, 21(1):37–46.

D. Bates, M. Mächler, B. Bolker, and S. Walker. 2014. Fitting linear mixed-effects models using lme4. ArXiv preprint arXiv:1406.5823.

G. Bossaert, H. Colpin, S.J. Pijl, and K. Petry. 2015. Quality of reciprocated friendships of students with special educational needs in mainstream seventh grade. *Exceptionality*, 23(1):54–72.

T.L. Chartrand and J.A. Bargh. 1999. The chameleon effect: the perception–behavior link and social interaction. *Journal of personality and social psychology*, 76(6):893.

K. Cornish, N. Rinehart, K. Gray, and P. Howlin. 2010. *Comic strip task*. Monash University Developmental Neuroscience and Genetic Disorders Laboratory and Monash University Centre for Developmental Psychiatry and Psychology, Melbourne.

Michelle Dean, Robin Harwood, and Connie Kasari. 2017. The art of camouflage: Gender differences in the social behaviors of girls and boys with autism spectrum disorder. *Autism*, 21(6):678–689.

E.A. Demetriou, A. Lampit, D.S. Quintana, S.L. Naismith, Y.J.C. Song, J.E. Pye, and A.J. Guastella. 2018. Autism spectrum disorders: a meta-analysis of executive function. *Molecular psychiatry*, 23(5):1198–1204.

J. Deng, N. Cummins, M. Schmitt, K. Qian, F. Ringeval, and B. Schuller. 2017-07. Speech-based diagnosis of autism spectrum condition by generative adversarial network representations. In *Proceedings of the 2017 International Conference on Digital Health*, page 53–57.

Maureen S Durkin, Matthew J Maenner, Jon Baio, Deborah Christensen, Julie Daniels, Robert Fitzgerald, Pamela Imm, Li-Ching Lee, Laura A Schieve, Kim Van Naarden Braun, et al. 2017. Autism spectrum disorder among us children (2002–2010): Socioeconomic, racial, and ethnic disparities. *American journal of public health*, 107(11):1818–1826.

J.H. Elder, C.M. Kreider, S.N. Brasher, and M. Ansell. 2017. Clinical impact of early diagnosis of autism on the prognosis and parent–child relationships. *Psychology research and behavior management*.

E. Fernell, M.A. Eriksson, and C. Gillberg. 2013. Early diagnosis of autism and impact on prognosis: a narrative review. *Clinical epidemiology*, 5:33.

P. Fitzpatrick, J.A. Frazier, D. Cochran, T. Mitchell, C. Coleman, and R.C. Schmidt. 2018. Relationship between theory of mind, emotion recognition, and social synchrony in adolescents with and without autism. *Frontiers in psychology*, 9:1337.

M.A. Gernsbacher and M. Yergeau. 2019. Empirical failures of the claim that autistic people lack a theory of mind. *Archives of scientific psychology*, 7(1):102.

G.A. Gioia, P.K. Isquith, S.C. Guy, and L. Kenworthy. 2000. *Behavior rating inventory of executive function: BRIEF*. Psychological Assessment Resources, Odessa, FL.

Judith Gould and Jacqui Ashton-Smith. 2011. Missed diagnosis or misdiagnosis? girls and women on the autism spectrum. *Good Autism Practice (GAP)*, 12(1):34–41.

B. Heasman and A. Gillespie. 2018. Perspective-taking is two-sided: Misunderstandings between people with asperger's syndrome and their family members. *Autism*, 22(6):740–750.

S. Koehne, A. Hatri, J.T. Cacioppo, and I. Dziobek. 2016. Perceived interpersonal synchrony increases empathy: insights from autism spectrum disorder. *Cognition*, 146:8–15.

S. Kousidis, D. Dorran, Y. Wang, B. Vaughan, C. Cullen, D. Campbell, and E. Coyle. 2008. Towards measuring continuous acoustic feature convergence in unconstrained spoken dialogues. In *Ninth Annual Conference of the International Speech Communication Association*.

Joanna Kruyt and Štefan Beňuš. 2021. Prosodic entrainment in individuals with autism spectrum disorder. *Topics in Linguistics*, 22(2):47–61.

A. Kuznetsova, P.B. Brockhoff, and R.H.B. Christensen. 2017. lmertest package: Tests in linear mixed effects models. *Journal of Statistical Software*, 82(13):1–26.

H.Y. Lee, T.Y. Hu, H. Jing, Y.F. Chang, Y. Tsao, Y.C. Kao, and T.L. Pao. 2013. Ensemble of machine learning and acoustic segment model techniques for speech emotion and autism spectrum disorders recognition. In *INTERSPEECH*, page 215–219.

H. Lehnert-LeHouillier, S. Terrazas, and S. Sandoval. 2020. Prosodic entrainment in conversations of verbal children and teens on the autism spectrum. *Frontiers in Psychology*, 11:2718.

R. Levitan, A. Gravano, and J. Hirschberg. 2011-06. Entrainment in speech preceding backchannels. In *Proceedings of the 49th Annual Meeting of the Association for Computational Linguistics: Human Language Technologies*, page 113–117.

C. Looze and S. Rauzy. 2009. Automatic detection and prediction of topic changes through automatic detection of register variations and pause duration. In *Interspeech 2009*.

C. Lord, M. Rutter, P.C. DiLavore, S. Risi, K. Gotham, and S.L. Bishop. 2008. *Autism diagnostic observation schedule (ADOS): Manual*. Western Psychological Services, Los Angeles.

K.L. Marsh, R.W. Isenhower, M.J. Richardson, M. Helt, A.D. Verbalis, R.C. Schmidt, and D. Fein. 2013. Autism and social disconnection in interpersonal rocking. *Frontiers in integrative neuroscience*, 7:4.

J. Michalsky, H. Schoormann, and O. Niebuhr. 2018. Conversational quality is affected by and reflected in prosodic entrainment. In *International Conference on Speech Prosody*, page 389–392.

D.E. Milton. 2012. On the ontological status of autism: the 'double empathy problem'. *Disability Society*, 27(6):883–887.

A. Nadig and H. Shaw. 2012. Acoustic and perceptual measurement of expressive prosody in high-functioning autism: Increased pitch range and what it means to listeners. *Journal of Autism and Developmental Disorders*, 42(4):499–511.

T. Nakano, N. Kato, and S. Kitazawa. 2011. Lack of eyeblink entrainments in autism spectrum disorders. *Neuropsychologia*, 49(9):2784–2790.

J.P. Noel, M.A. Niear, N.S. Lazzara, and M.T. Wallace. 2017. Uncoupling between multisensory temporal function and nonverbal turn-taking in autism spectrum disorder. *IEEE Transactions on cognitive and developmental systems*, 10(4):973–982.

K. Ochi, N. Ono, K. Owada, M. Kojima, M. Kuroda, S. Sagayama, and H. Yamasue. 2019. Quantification of speech and synchrony in the conversation of adults with autism spectrum disorder. *PloS one*, 14(12):0225377.

J.S. Pardo, R. Gibbons, A. Suppes, and R.M. Krauss. 2012. Phonetic convergence in college roommates. *Journal of Phonetics*, 40(1):190–197.

J. Parish-Morris, M. Liberman, N. Ryant, C. Cieri, L. Bateman, E. Ferguson, and R.T. Schultz. 2016. Exploring autism spectrum disorders using hlt. In *Proceedings of the conference. Association for Computational Linguistics. Meeting*, page 74. NIH Public Access.

Shivani P Patel, Jennifer Cole, Joseph CY Lau, Gabrielle Fragnito, and Molly Losh. 2022. Verbal entrainment in autism spectrum disorder and first-degree relatives. *Scientific reports*, 12(1):11496.

R. Paul, S.M. Orlovski, H.C. Marcinko, and F. Volkmar. 2009. Conversational behaviors in youth with high-functioning asd and asperger syndrome. *Journal of autism and developmental disorders*, 39(1):115–125.

J.M. Paynter, D. Keen, and V.J. Rose. 2016. Systematic review documents limited empirical support for the practical application of the theory of mind model of asd. *Evidence-Based Communication Assessment and Intervention*, 10(3-4):131–139.

M Pedersen, ABA Agersted, and A Jønsson. 2015. Aspects of adolescence and voice: Girls versus boys–a review. *J Child Adolesc Behav*, 3(211):2.

U.D. Reichel, Š. Beňuš, and K. Mády. 2018. Entrainment profiles: Comparison by gender, role, and feature set. *Speech Communication*, 100:46–57.

E. Sheppard, D. Pillai, G.T.L. Wong, D. Ropar, and P. Mitchell. 2016. How easy is it to read the minds of people with autism spectrum disorder? *Journal of autism and developmental disorders*, 46(4):1247–1254.

H. Tager-Flusberg. 2007. Evaluating the theory-of-mind hypothesis of autism. *Current directions in psychological science*, 16(6):311–315.

A. Taheri, A. Perry, and P. Minnes. 2016. Examining the social participation of children and adolescents with intellectual disabilities and autism spectrum disorder in relation to peers. *Journal of Intellectual Disability Research*, 60(5):435–443.

E.E. Watkins, Z.J. Zimmermann, and A. Poling. 2014. The gender of participants in published research involving people with autism spectrum disorders. *Research in Autism Spectrum Disorders*, 8(2):143–146.

Receptive Language Development Intervention and Assessment in Conversational Interactions with QTrobot for Autism

Aida Nazari and **Sviatlana Höhn** and **Ali Paikan** and **Pouyan Ziafati**
LuxAI S.A., Boulevard Royal 22, Luxembourg, Luxembourg

Abstract

Delays in language development in early childhood are usually the first hints that motivate parents to initiate autism diagnostics. While expressive language can be easily observed, assessment of receptive language development is more difficult and prone to misjudgement. Robot-assisted autism interventions offer a potential solution. This article describes the results of long-term use of QTrobot for autism at home by multiple families. The setup is non-experimental and thus, the results are ecologically valid. The results of this exploratory analysis show that playful interactions with QTrobot for autism help to perform a more accurate assessment of the child's receptive vocabulary. The results also suggest that QTrobot for autism supports autistic children in receptive language learning.

1 Introduction

Language development delays are frequently a key concern for parents seeking a diagnosis related to neurodevelopmental disorders such as Autism (Gernsbacher et al., 2016). It has been shown that improving communication skill of autistic children can improve their long-term prognosis and improve their chances for independent living and skill acquisition in other areas of development (Hendricks, 2010; Gray et al., 2014). Hence, improving their child's communication abilities is one of the primary goals for parents seeking support.

Numerous studies indicate that autistic children experience delays in both expressive (language production) and receptive (language comprehension) language skills (Gernsbacher et al., 2016). They tend to have a smaller vocabulary and struggle with understanding and using language effectively. Speech therapy can improve language development, but it is expensive and sometimes inaccessible for families. In addition, inaccurate evaluation of the child's language leads to resource overuse in terms of budget and time.

While it is observable which words a child can say, personalized interventions targeting receptive language skills can pose challenges due to assessment accuracy in which parents become a proxy to evaluate their children's language skills using tools like the MacArthur Bates (Luyster et al., 2007) or Vineland Adaptive Behavior Scales (VABS) assessments (Sparrow and Cicchetti, 1989). However, studies indicate that parents frequently misjudge their child's receptive language skills (Feldman et al., 2000; Akhtar and Gernsbacher, 2007). Further challenges for assessment of receptive language skills include difficulties to differentiate between lack of skills and lack of motivation and long waiting periods for professional assessment.

To overcome these barriers in assessment and to support autistic children in developing better receptive language skills, one effective approach is to involve and empower parents in interventions. Numerous approaches focus on educating parents to deliver parent-led interventions, such as parent-driven Early Start Denver Model (P-ESDM) (Abouzeid et al., 2020), which emphasizes supporting parents to bridge the gap in accessibility of autism interventions. However, parent-led interventions often necessitate professional-led training, supervision, and significant effort from parents to be effective, particularly in enhancing children's receptive language development skills.

Robot-assisted interventions represent a relatively new field that aims to enhance the accessibility, evidence-based nature, and reliability of standard interventions (Salimi et al., 2021; Kouroupa et al., 2022). These interventions can effectively support parents in contributing to their child's education with reduced effort and improved outcomes. QTrobot for autism is one such technology.

The objective of this article is to evaluate the outcome of the QTRobot for Autism in receptive language assessment at the start of its use as compared to parents' judgement, and the receptive lan-

Proceedings of the First ICARD Workshop, pages 12–16
September 12, 2023 ©2023 Association for Computational Linguistics

guage skill development after $6 - 12$ months of use by five families who were Beta-testers of the platform. The next section describes QTrobot for Autism curriculum including the method for receptive language development. Further, we explain the data and present the analysis results regarding receptive language assessment and development in the selected user's population. Finally, we draw conclusions and outline future research directions.

2 QTrobot for Autism

QTrobot for Autism incorporates a humanoid, expressive robot programmed with a curriculum with over 400 activities targeting various skill areas, including social, emotional, self-regulation and cognitive skills, and receptive and expressive language development. The curriculum is based on neurodevelopmental milestones in pediatrics and integrates evidence-based methods such as social narratives, Discrete Trial Training, prompting, reinforcement, visual supports, and video modeling. Each milestone is used as a unique unit, practicing the tasks that help the child to achieve that milestone. For example, a 2-years old child is expected to be able to point to minimum 2 body parts when they are named, therefore the curriculum includes a unit focused on identification of body parts in it's level 2 covering the developmental age of 12 to 24 months.

2.1 Skill Assessment at Baseline

At start, parents are asked to complete a placement quiz and conservatively rank their child's skills from 1 (the child cannot do that) to 3 (the child can always do this). Based on the quiz results, a set of educational activities is suggested as the starting point in the curriculum. Conservative ranking ensures that areas of doubt are evaluated later using the robot. This approach minimizes the risk of overlooking early developmental milestones. Examples of assessment units are: "My child can point to a particular color if I name it" and "My child can discriminate between big and small items, when presented in real life or in pictures".

2.2 QTrobot Curriculum Use Procedure

During each session, parents use the Educator tablet to select the activities identified through the parent quiz. The robot then leads the activity, providing instructions, age-appropriate questions, and visual stimuli to support learning. For receptive language skills, the robot presents stimuli on the Learner tablet, and the child responds by selecting provided options. Figure 1 shows the triadic set-up of the interaction.

Figure 1: The triadic setup in interactions with QTrobot for Autism: Child, parent and robot.

In case of a corrrect response, the robot provides positive feedback using facial expressions, gestures, and language. If the response is incorrect, the robot provides structured prompts to help the child find the correct answer, then presenting a distractor trial using the skills from lower developmental age, followed by a repetition of the original question. Structured prompting ensures systematic teaching and prevents trial-and-error learning, while the error correction procedure without negative feedback ensures that challenging instructions are reinforced after the child successfully responds with guidance. Once a skill has been practiced with over 90% success rate for three consecutive practices, the robot marks it as mastered, prompting parents to introduce a new skill from the same category. The robot collects data on task performance in a privacy-preserving way, and maintains a record of each child's progress. These data serve as a reliable source for objective evaluation, i.e. in assessing the child's receptive language repertoire.

As part of the intervention, parents receive training sessions, support calls, video and written resources and instructions on how to create additional practice opportunities outside of robot interactions, helping their children generalize skills to natural environments and maintain acquired skills over time.

2.3 Receptive Language Curriculum

Also in the receptive language curriculum, each unit is connected to one particular developmental milestone in terms of how language is developed in neurotypical children. For example, at certain points in the development, experts in language development expect children to understand certain words, adjectives, prepositions and verb-noun combinations. We have used these developmental milestones as the guideline for the curriculum units and tasks and in the placement questionnaires. Using this method of arrangement of units, we can create an individual educational plan for each child.

QTrobot supports receptive language development in several ways. Direct interaction with QTrobot and practicing receptive language questions improves a child's language comprehension. Second, parents learn how structured receptive language training is organized and delivered, and how to replicate them without the robot. In addition, by observing the robot sessions and participating actively in them, parents are informed about their child's receptive language ability. In this way, parents are better informed when it comes to answering parental questionnaires to evaluate a child's receptive language ability.

3 Procedure and Results

To evaluate the expected impact, an exploratory post market analysis has been conducted on five families who purchased the robot in 2021 as Beta-testers, when QTrobot for Autism was released for parents for the first time. All on-boarded families already received therapy for their children. The minimum physical age of children was 4 and the maximum was 11 years, and the developmental age of 18-24 months. We use the single subject study method evaluating the progress of each child based on their baseline when starting the intervention according to their parents ranking of receptive language in the placement quiz. The goals during the Beta-testing phase, in which families were granted free of charge use of QTrobot for six months, included

1. Feasibility evaluation of at home implementation of robot-assisted interventions;
2. Parents ability to follow instructions and deliver the intervention with fidelity;
3. Monitoring of skill acquisition and generalisation by children;
4. Monitoring for undesired behaviours and any negative side effects related to the robot;
5. Monitoring the long-term effectiveness after the novelty effect decreases.

ID	Av. Q	Av. RL Q
P01	398	122
P01	423	116
P03	1071	237
P04	579	188
P05	454	152
TT	585	163

Table 1: ID: learner ID; Av. T Q: monthly average number of non-unique questions played by the earner from the entire curriculum; Av. RL Q: monthly average number of receptive language questions played. Last row: total average over selected learners.

In addition to these set goals, the platform enabled a more accurate assessment of language development by both robot and parents, as our analysis here shows.

We evaluated of the data collected by the robot from the sessions with children conducted by their parents at home. In addition, video statements submitted by parents after a duration of use between 6 and 12 months, have been used to evaluate parents perception of impact on various levels. Appendix A provides links to the videos.

The total use of QTrobot for each family was more than 12 months. Each unit includes eight questions which can be repeated if a child cannot reply correctly and independently for the first time, according the the methodology explained in Sec. 2.2. Table 1 shows average use of QTrobot curriculum and receptive language curriculum in 2021. The data shows that each family has played in 2021 in average 163 questions of receptive language development per month, and in average 585 questions on all skills, including emotional, social, expressive and cognitive. Because the families followed the methodology described in Section 2, they played more advanced questions after they mastered the preceding ones. By the end of 12 months of use, all five subjects mastered the level 3, and four subjects also mastered level 4. Thus, the developmental age of all the kids in terms of receptive language has evolved to up to 4 years, as compared with the developmental age of about 2 years at start. Figure 2 shows and example of a lerner's answer history. Figure 3 shows how a learner's success can be measured over time.

In addition to the learner data, video reports from parents were analyzed and annotated according to three categories: ease of use, effectiveness on child's learning from parents perspective and ef-

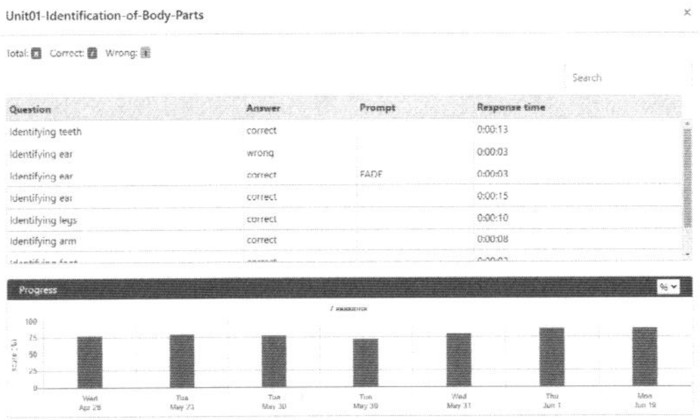

Figure 2: A learner answers a question with error. The question is simplified. The answer is then correct. The material is rehearsed.

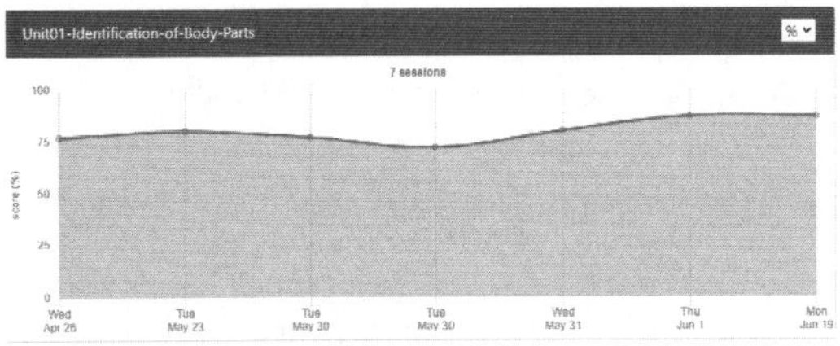

Figure 3: Skill development with QTrobot over time.

fectiveness on improving parents knowledge of the child's developments.

We found evidence in our data confirming earlier findings in literature that parents tend to misjudge their children's receptive language skills (Feldman et al., 2000; Akhtar and Gernsbacher, 2007). For example, one of the parents mentions in the video that she thought that her child is already good at understanding words, but she followed the recommendation from LuxAI team to start with earlier levels of curriculum, and realized that the child's actual developmental level in receptive language was actually lower.

The analysis of the data and the parents videos with respect to the receptive language development shows that:
1) All children have mastered receptive language skills, showing progress compared to their baseline evaluation. We can conclude that children can learn effectively from the robot, and they can show progress in terms of increased developmental age in receptive language development area.
2) The robot can generate reliable data related to the children's receptive language ability, which can be used for intervention planning.
3) Parents tend to misjudge their child's receptive language skills (over- and underestimation).
4) By involving parents in the sessions and allowing them to observe their children in concrete language tasks, they would be able to have a more accurate understanding of their child's strengths and weaknesses and therefore they can be a more reliable proxy for evaluation of the child's language for purposes such as intervention planning.

All parents found the robot effective in supporting them to deliver interventions and in gaining a deeper knowledge about their child's educational and developmental status.

4 Conclusions and Future Work

This article focused on receptive language assessment and development in autistic children, and presented the results of non-experimental long-term Beta-use of QTrobot for Autism in families. Data collected by the robot from sessions with children and customer feedback videos have shown that even parents without technical backgrounds can easily utilize the robot at home to provide structured interventions and support their child's development. Beyond its educational role, parents have reported that QTrobot indirectly enhances their knowledge of their child's developmental progress and increases their understanding of evidence-based interventions for receptive language skills. By observing their child's performance in each task and witnessing how the robot delivers simple instructions, reinforcement, and structured prompts, parents gain valuable insights. Consequently, QTrobot empowers parents, enabling them to reliably participate as proxies in assessments by better understanding their child's strengths and needs.

Additionally, QTrobot provides reporting and progress monitoring features, capturing data on task performance and maintaining a record of each child's progress. This data serves as a reliable source for objective evaluation, such as assessing a child's receptive language repertoire. Professionals and speech therapists can use this information to accurately evaluate a child for individually tailored interventions. Even though that the robot is still expensive, it is far more affordable and accessible solution than speech therapy and it can bring several added benefits including improving parents ability to teach speech/communication skills, developing a better understanding of the child's ability and perform better as a proxy, and as a consequence, minimizing inaccurate resource allocation caused by imprecise evaluation for the child.

However, there are certain limitations to consider regarding the interventions provided by QTrobot for autism, as well as the presentation of data to parents and professionals. Currently, QTrobot employs a set of stimuli designed to address specific areas of receptive language development, randomly presenting eight stimuli during each activity session. To enhance effectiveness, future iterations should aim to develop an automated recommendation system that considers each child's previous performance to select more relevant stimuli to further individualize the educational interaction. For instance, in an activity focused on discrimination of size adjectives, the algorithm could prioritize presenting more stimuli related to identifying small items if a child struggles in that area.

Furthermore, the robot currently presents data in the form of the percentage of correctly answered questions during interactions, generating progress reports based on this percentage. It also provides detailed reports that include the stimuli presented to the child and their responses. While this enables evaluation of a child's receptive language skills and creates profiles of nouns, verbs, adjectives, and prepositions they comprehend accurately, it would be advantageous to align QTrobot's data reporting with standardized language assessment tools commonly used in speech therapy and other interventions. The manufacturer plans to conduct clinical studies aiming at direct evaluation of child language using standardized language development tests and develop an algorithm that maps QTrobot's raw data to these standardized measures.

Acknowledgements

Dr. Sviatlana Höhn thanks Fonds National de la Recherche Luxembourg for their support. Industrial Fellowship grant number 17762538.

References

Nadia Abouzeid, Mélina Rivard, Catherine Mello, Zakaria Mestari, Mélina Boulé, and Claudia Guay. 2020. Parent coaching intervention program based on the early start denver model for children with autism spectrum disorder: Feasibility and acceptability study. *Research in Developmental Disabilities*, 105:103747.

Nameera Akhtar and Morton Ann Gernsbacher. 2007. Joint attention and vocabulary development: A critical look. *Language and linguistics compass*, 1(3):195–207.

Heidi M Feldman, Christine A Dollaghan, Thomas F Campbell, Marcia Kurs-Lasky, Janine E Janosky, and Jack L Paradise. 2000. Measurement properties of the macarthur communicative development inventories at ages one and two years. *Child development*, 71(2):310–322.

Morton Ann Gernsbacher, Emily M Morson, and Elizabeth J Grace. 2016. Language development in autism. In *Neurobiology of language*, pages 879–886. Elsevier.

Kylie M Gray, Caroline M Keating, John R Taffe, Avril V Brereton, Stewart L Einfeld, Tessa C Reardon, and Bruce J Tonge. 2014. Adult outcomes in autism: Community inclusion and living skills. *Journal of autism and developmental disorders*, 44:3006–3015.

Dawn Hendricks. 2010. Employment and adults with autism spectrum disorders: Challenges and strategies for success. *Journal of vocational rehabilitation*, 32(2):125–134.

Athanasia Kouroupa, Keith R Laws, Karen Irvine, Silvana E Mengoni, Alister Baird, and Shivani Sharma. 2022. The use of social robots with children and young people on the autism spectrum: A systematic review and meta-analysis. *Plos one*, 17(6):e0269800.

Rhiannon Luyster, Kristina Lopez, and Catherine Lord. 2007. Characterizing communicative development in children referred for autism spectrum disorders using the macarthur-bates communicative development inventory (cdi). *Journal of child language*, 34(3):623–654.

Zohreh Salimi, Ensiyeh Jenabi, and Saeid Bashirian. 2021. Are social robots ready yet to be used in care and therapy of autism spectrum disorder: A systematic review of randomized controlled trials. *Neuroscience & Biobehavioral Reviews*, 129:1–16.

Sara S Sparrow and Domenic V Cicchetti. 1989. *The Vineland adaptive behavior scales.* Allyn & Bacon.

Limitations

The results described in this article come from a non-experimental setup and need further validation in a clinical study.

Ethics Statement

The data used for this article were obtained and analysed with informed consent based on the QTrobot for autism terms of use and a separate agreement with the parents.

A Parents' Reports

https://youtu.be/ufJI2rnCAxE
https://youtu.be/DwLBI5vtuC0
https://youtu.be/f8RURWsANbI
https://youtu.be/jgspU4QV_7M
https://youtu.be/Lhzx9qo4sN4

Computational Analysis of Backchannel Usage and Overlap Length in Autistic Children

Grace O. Lawley[1], **Peter A. Heeman**[1], **Steven Bedrick**[2]
[1]*Computer Science and Engineering*
[2]*Department of Medical Informatics and Clinical Epidemiology*
Oregon Health & Science University, Portland, OR, USA

Abstract

Backchanneling (e.g., *right*, *okay*, *uhhuh*) during a dialogue signals that a person is engaged and following along with what is being said. Although backchannels often overlap with other utterances, they are not interpreted as an attempt to take the floor when used successfully. Limited work has been done on investigating the frequency and overlap length of backchannels in the language of Autistic children. After controlling for age, sex, and IQ, we found that Autistic children used significantly less backchannels than their Typically Developing (TD) peers. Additionally, we found that Autistic children were less likely than TD children to produce a backchannel with a greater overlap length.

1 Introduction

Providing feedback to your conversational partner in the form of backchanneling is a pervasive component of verbal communication. A backchannel is a short utterance (e.g., *mmhmm*, *yes*, *uhhuh*) said by person A while person B continues to have the floor (Levinson and Torreira, 2015). Although these brief utterances do not contribute new meaning to the dialogue, they still contribute important pragmatic information; by using a backchannel, a person is signaling that they are engaged and following along but that they also understand the other person is not ready to yield the floor. Backchannels sometimes (but not always) overlap other utterances (Levinson and Torreira, 2015).

Deficits in backchanneling ability could lead to miscommunications or problems related to turn-taking. An extended pause before a backchannel could cause the backchannel to be interpreted as negative rather than positive (e.g., an excessive pause before saying *okay*). Starting a backchannel too close to the end of the other speaker's utterance could be interpreted as an attempt to take the floor (Schegloff, 2000).

Autism Spectrum Disorder (ASD) is a developmental condition characterized by difficulties with social communication (American Psychiatric Association, 2013). These difficulties often include problems with pragmatic language, with Autistic[1] children frequently having difficulties with conversational reciprocity, such as turn taking and filler usage (Baltaxe and D'Angiola, 1992; Paul et al., 2009). Computational methods have been used before to successfully capture differences between Autistic and Typically Developing (TD) children for fillers and mazes (Parish-Morris et al., 2017; Salem et al., 2021; Lawley et al., 2022).

Another way these difficulties could manifest is in backchannel usage. While some work has been done on examining differences in backchannel usage in ASD before (Heeman et al., 2010; Lunsford et al., 2012), previous investigations have been limited by small sample size, few female participants, and lack of controlling for participant-level variables such as age, sex, and intellectual ability. Furthermore, to our knowledge, previous work has not examined backchanneling in combination with overlap length.

In this paper we investigate whether Autistic children use backchannels at different rates their TD peers using a multivariate approach that allows us to control for potential confounding participant-level variables such as age, sex, and IQ. Since Autistic children frequently have difficulties with pragmatic language skills, we hypothesize that the ASD group will use less backchannels than the TD group. We also investigate whether group differences in backchannel rates are affected by whether the backchannel is an overlapping utterance and the length of the overlap (if any). Assuming that producing an overlapping-backchannel requires better

[1]We are using identity-first language (i.e., Autistic children) here instead of person-first language (i.e., children with Autism) as the former is the current preference among many Autistic individuals (Brown, n.d.).

Proceedings of the First ICARD Workshop, pages 17–23
September 12, 2023

turn-taking abilities than producing a backchannel that does not overlap, we hypothesize that the ASD group will produce less overlapping-backchannels and the ones they do produce will have a shorter overlap length.

2 Methods

2.1 Dataset

Analyses were performed on language samples of 116 ASD children and 65 TD children between 4 to 15 years old. All were native English speakers and had an IQ ≥ 70. Intellectual ability was estimated using the Wechsler Intelligence Scale for Children, fourth edition (WISC-IV; Wechsler, 2003) for children 7 years and older; for children younger than 7 years old, the Wechsler Preschool and Primary Scale of Intelligence, third edition (WPPSI-III; Wechsler, 2002) was used instead. Overall language ability and pragmatic and structural language skills were measured using the Children's Communication Checklist, version 2 (CCC-2; Bishop, 2003). A complete summary of the demographic and clinical sample characteristics for all 181 children is reported in Appendix A.

2.2 Language Samples

Analyses were performed on transcribed Autism Diagnostic Observation Schedule (ADOS) sessions (Lord et al., 2000). All children were administered the ADOS-2, Module 3. Scoring was completed using the revised algorithms (Gotham et al., 2009). Sessions were transcribed by a team of trained transcribers according to modified Systematic Analysis of Language Transcript (SALT) guidelines (Miller and Iglesias, 2012).

Transcribers were instructed to include one of the following five punctuation marks at the end of each utterance: '.', '?', '!', '$>$', '$\wedge$'. Transcribers used '$>$' for abandoned utterances and '$\wedge$' for interrupted utterances. Spans of overlapping speech were surrounded by angled brackets: $< >$. Four ADOS activities were selected for this analysis: *Emotions*; *Social Difficulties and Annoyance*; *Friends, Relationships and Marriage*; *Loneliness*. These activities were chosen because of their conversational structure and similarities to naturalistic dialogue.

2.3 Backchannels

For each child, we calculated the total number of utterances that were backchannels. We considered an utterance to be a backchannel if it (1) appeared in the following, predefined list: *mmhmm*, *yes*, *ok*, *uhhuh*, *right*, *yeah*, *yep*; (2) was not the first utterance of the transcript; (3) did not follow a question (i.e., its predecessor utterance, as defined in section 2.4, was not a question). Creation of the predefined list of backchannels was informed by spelling conventions followed by our transcription team for words that commonly occur in natural conversation. These spelling conventions were strictly followed during transcription. We omitted utterances that immediately followed a question to avoid catching instances where words such as *yes* and *yeah* were used as an affirmative reply to a question. Overall, there were a total of 1,187 backchannels: 753 *yeah*; 223 *mmhmm*; 75 *yes*; 49 *yep*; 43 *ok*; 34 *uhhuh*; 10 *right*.

There were a total of 1,807 utterances that satisfied criteria (1) and (2) but not (3). To test the validity of our rule of omitting these utterances, we took a random sample of 200 utterances from this subset (100 for each diagnostic group) and manually checked each. Of the 200 random utterances, 2 were false positives (i.e., were backchannels) and 198 were true negatives (i.e., were not backchannels), giving us a false positive rate of 0.01.

2.4 Overlap Length

For a given utterance, we defined the overlap length as the amount (in seconds) that it overlaps with its predecessor utterance. We followed the process detailed by Lunsford et al. (2016) to identify the predecessors of each utterance. Given an utterance u, let u' be the previous utterance said by the same speaker. Let w be the most recent utterance said by the second speaker (i.e., start time of $w <$ start time of u). Whichever of u' and w has the later end time is the predecessor of u. Not every utterance is a predecessor utterance and a single utterance can be the predecessor for multiple utterances. The initial utterance in a transcript will not have a predecessor. An example of predecessor utterances in practice is shown in Figure 1.

After identifying the predecessors for each utterance, we can proceed with calculating the overlap length (if any) of each utterance and its predecessor. We first subtracted the end time of the predecessor from the start time of the utterance. If the resulting value is positive (i.e., a pause or gap), the overlap length is 0. If instead the resulting value is negative (i.e., an overlap), the overlap length is the absolute

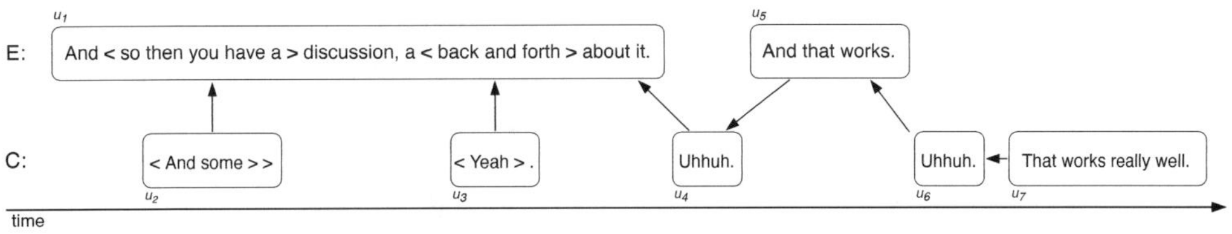

Figure 1: Example of predecessor utterances. Arrows point towards the predecessor of a given utterance. Abbreviations: E = Examiner; C = Child.

value of this number.

2.5 Overlapping-backchannels

We defined an overlapping-backchannel as an utterance that is (1) a backchannel and (2) overlaps its predecessor utterance by more than 200 ms. By this definition, overlapping-backchannels are a subset of backchannels. We used a cutoff of 200 ms to account for any overlaps that can be attributed to reaction time delays (Fry, 1975; Levinson and Torreira, 2015).

2.6 Statistical Analysis

We first compared the rates of both backchannels (total backchannels / total utterances) and overlapping-backchannels (total overlapping-backchannels / total utterances) between the ASD and TD groups without incorporating additional participant-level variables. Since normality assumptions were not met (Shapiro-Wilk Normality test; $p < .001$), we used the nonparametric Wilcoxon-Mann-Whitney test to compare groups. The dependent variable was backchannel or overlapping-backchannel rate and the independent variable was diagnosis (ASD; TD). We used rank-biserial correlations (r_{rb}; interpretation: small = 0.10-0.29, medium = 0.30-0.49, large = 0.50-1.0) to calculate effect size (Cureton, 1956; Wendt, 1972).

Next, to investigate group differences in backchannel rates while also taking into account the participants' age, sex, and IQ as well as overlap length, we fit a mixed effects logistic regression model. The binary response variable was created as follows: with the data formatted as one utterance per row, each backchannel was coded as 1 and every other utterance was coded as 0. A per-participant random intercept was included since each participant was associated with multiple utterances. The primary predictor variable was diagnosis (ASD; TD). The other predictor variables included were participants' age, sex, and IQ and the utterance overlap length. Additionally, an interaction term between diagnosis and overlap length was included. All continuous variables were transformed into z-scores prior to model estimation.

Lastly, we repeated our second experiment but for just the overlapping-backchannels. To create the binary response variable, each overlapping-backchannel was coded as 1 and every other utterance was coded as 0. We did not include a diagnosis and overlap length interaction term in this model since the results of Analysis of Variance (ANOVA) showed that the inclusion of an interaction term did not significantly contribute to the model.

All analyses were performed using the statistical programming language R (R Core Team, 2020). The lme4 package (Bates et al., 2015) was used to create the mixed effects logistic regression models.

3 Results

Figure 2 shows the distribution of both the backchannel and overlapping-backchannel rates within each diagnostic group.

The median and interquartile range (IQR) values and the results from the Wilcoxon-Mann-Whitney tests for backchannel and overlapping-backchannel rates are reported in Table 1. There was a significant difference in backchannel usage between the ASD and TD groups ($p = .001$; small effect size: $r_{rb} = .298$). The ASD group used less backchannels than the TD group overall (ASD = .025 [.011, .042] < TD = .039 [.022, .066]). For overlapping-backchannels, there was also a significant group difference ($p < .001$; medium effect size: $r_{rb} = .397$), with the ASD group producing less overlapping-backchannels than the TD group (ASD = .001 [.000, .007] < TD = .009 [.000, .018]).

Next, the results of the mixed effects logistic regression model for backchannel usage are reported in Table 2. A significant group difference in backchannel usage was still found after adjusting

	ASD	TD	U	p	r_{rb}
backchannels	.025 [.011, .042]	.039 [.022, .066]	2645.5	.001	.298
overlapping-backchannels	.001 [.000, .007]	.009 [.000, .018]	2273.0	< .001	.397

Table 1: Backchannel and overlapping-backchannel usage rates by diagnostic group.

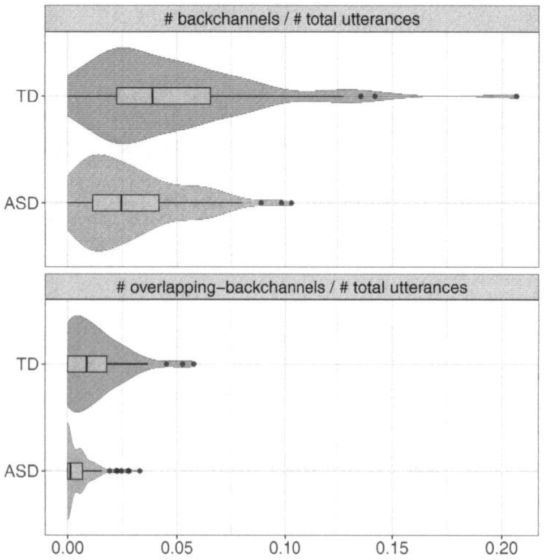

Figure 2: Distributions of backchannel and overlapping-backchannel rates by diagnosis. The x-axis (shared by both plots) is the proportion of backchannels or overlapping-backchannels said by a child. Behind the boxplots are violin plots. Violin plots are mirrored kernel density plots, where wider areas correspond to a higher density of observations.

for age, sex, IQ, and overlap length ($\chi^2 = -3.212$, $P = .001$, Table 2). As before, the ASD had a lower backchannel rate than the TD group. There was no significant effect on backchannel rate of participant age, sex, or IQ. Overlap length significantly contributed to backchannel rate ($\chi^2 = 9.651$, $P < .001$), with overlap length increasing the likelihood that an utterance is a backchannel. There was also a significant interaction between diagnosis and overlap length ($\chi^2 = -2.216$, $P = .027$), with the ASD group being less likely to produce a backchannel as the overlap length increases.

Lastly, the results of the mixed effects logistic regression model for overlapping-backchannels are reported in Table 3. For this model, inclusion of an interaction term between diagnosis and overlap length did not significantly contribute to the model so the interaction was left out. After controlling for age, sex, IQ, and overlap length, a significant group difference in overlapping-backchannel usage remained ($\chi^2 = -3.990$, $P < .001$), with the ASD group again using less backchannels than the TD group. The age, sex, and IQ of the participants had no significant effect on overlapping-backchannel rate. The overlap length significantly effected the likelihood that an utterance was an overlapping-backchannel (χ^2 = 19.496, $P < .001$), irrespective of participant's age, sex, IQ, or diagnosis. In other words, the longer the overlap, the more likely that an utterance was an overlapping-backchannel.

	Log-odds	S.E.	χ^2	$P(\chi^2)$
(Intercept)	-3.233	0.140		
Dx			-3.212	0.001
ASD	-0.496	0.154		
Sex			0.008	0.994
Male	0.001	0.149		
Age	0.025	0.067	0.375	0.708
IQ	-0.027	0.072	-0.379	0.705
Overlap	0.215	0.022	9.651	< 0.001
Dx:Overlap			-2.216	0.027
ASD:Overlap	-0.082	0.037		

Table 2: Mixed effects logistic regression model predicting likelihood of a backchannel utterance.

	Log-odds	S.E.	χ^2	$P(\chi^2)$
(Intercept)	-4.845	0.210		
Dx			-3.990	< 0.001
ASD	-0.949	0.238		
Sex			-0.765	0.444
Male	-0.176	0.229		
Age	-0.075	0.109	-0.690	0.490
IQ	-0.038	0.117	-0.328	0.743
Overlap	0.424	0.022	19.496	< 0.001

Table 3: Mixed effects logistic regression model predicting likelihood of an overlapping-backchannel utterance.

4 Conclusion

We investigated backchannel usage differences in language samples of Autistic and TD children and examined whether differences were associated with participant age, sex, IQ, or utterance length. We found that not only did the ASD group use backchannels and overlapping-backchannels at a significantly lower rate than the TD group, but that these differences were robust to participants' age, sex, and intellectual abilities.

We also explored the effect of overlap length between an utterance and its predecessor utterance. After accounting for diagnosis, age, sex, and IQ, utterances were more likely to be backchannels the more they overlapped with their corresponding predecessor utterance. The diagnostic group and overlap length interaction significantly effected the likelihood an utterance would be a backchannel, with the ASD group being less likely than the TD group to produce a backchannel with a greater overlap length.

These results suggest that Autistic children use backchannels less than TD children and that this difference is affected by whether the backchannel overlaps and how long the overlap is. This could indicate that the TD group is more skilled at timing backchannels since they produced more overlapping utterances than the ASD group. Our next steps including further refining our method of calculating overlap length and investigating the potential underlying language processes associated with this difference.

Ethics Statement

This study was approved by the Oregon Health & Science University IRB (Protocol #531) and all research was performed in accordance with their relevant guidelines and regulations.

Acknowledgements

This work was supported in part by the National Institute on Deafness and Other Communication Disorders of the NIH under Awards R01DC012033 (PI: Dr. E. Fombonne) and R01DC015999 (PIs: Dr. S. Bedrick & G. Fergadiotis).

References

American Psychiatric Association. 2013. *Diagnostic and Statistical Manual of Mental Disorders*, 5th edition.

Christiane A. M. Baltaxe and Nora D'Angiola. 1992. Cohesion in the discourse interaction of autistic, specifically language-impaired, and normal children. *Journal of Autism and Developmental Disorders*, 22(1):1–21.

Douglas Bates, Martin Mächler, Ben Bolker, and Steve Walker. 2015. Fitting Linear Mixed-Effects Models Using lme4. *Journal of Statistical Software*, 67(1):1–48.

Dorothy V. M. Bishop. 2003. *The Children's Communication Checklist, version 2 (CCC-2)*. Pearson, London.

Lydia Brown. n.d. Identity-First Language. Autistic Self Advocacy Network (ASAN). `https://autisticadvocacy.org/about-asan/identity-first-language/` Last accessed on 2023-05-10.

Edward E. Cureton. 1956. Rank-biserial correlation. *Psychometrika*, 21(3):287–290.

D.B. Fry. 1975. Simple Reaction-Times to Speech and Non-Speech Stimuli. *Cortex*, 11(4):355–360.

Katherine Gotham, Andrew Pickles, and Catherine Lord. 2009. Standardizing ADOS Scores for a Measure of Severity in Autism Spectrum Disorders. *Journal of Autism and Developmental Disorders*, 39(5):693–705.

Peter A. Heeman, Rebecca Lunsford, Ethan Selfridge, Lois Black, and Jan P. H. van Santen. 2010. Autism and Interactional Aspects of Dialogue. In *Proceedings of the SIGDIAL 2010 Conference*, pages 249–252, Tokyo, Japan. Association for Computational Linguistics.

Grace O. Lawley, Steven Bedrick, Heather MacFarlane, Jill K. Dolata, Alexandra C. Salem, and Eric Fombonne. 2022. "Um" and "Uh" Usage Patterns in Children with Autism: Associations with Measures of Structural and Pragmatic Language Ability. *Journal of Autism and Developmental Disorders*.

Stephen C. Levinson and Francisco Torreira. 2015. Timing in turn-taking and its implications for processing models of language. *Front. Psychol.*, 6(731).

Catherine Lord, Susan Risi, Linda Lambrecht, Edwin H. Cook, Bennett L. Leventhal, Pamela C. DiLavore, Andrew Pickles, and Michael Rutter. 2000. The Autism Diagnostic Observation Schedule, Generic: A Standard Measure of Social and Communication Deficits Associated with the Spectrum of Autism. *Journal of Autism and Developmental Disorders*, 30(3):205–223.

Rebecca Lunsford, Peter A. Heeman, and Emma Rennie. 2016. Measuring Turn-Taking Offsets in Human-Human Dialogues. In *Proc. Interspeech 2016*, pages 2895–2899.

Rebecca Lunsford, Peter A. Heeman, and Jan P. H. van Santen. 2012. Interactions Between Turn-taking Gaps, Disfluencies and Social Obligation. In *Proc. Interspeech 2012*, pages 607–610.

J. Miller and A. Iglesias. 2012. SALT: Systematic analysis of language transcripts [Research version]. *Middleton, WI: SALT Software*.

Julia Parish-Morris, Mark Y. Liberman, Christopher Cieri, John D. Herrington, Benjamin E. Yerys, Leila Bateman, Joseph Donaher, Emily Ferguson, Juhi

Pandey, and Robert T. Schultz. 2017. Linguistic camouflage in girls with autism spectrum disorder. *Molecular Autism*, 8(1):48–60.

Rhea Paul, Stephanie Miles Orlovski, Hillary Chuba Marcinko, and Fred Volkmar. 2009. Conversational Behaviors in Youth with High-functioning ASD and Asperger Syndrome. *Journal of Autism and Developmental Disorders*, 39(1):115–125.

R Core Team. 2020. *R: A Language and Environment for Statistical Computing*. R Foundation for Statistical Computing, Vienna, Austria.

Alexandra C. Salem, Heather MacFarlane, Joel R. Adams, Grace O. Lawley, Jill K. Dolata, Steven Bedrick, and Eric Fombonne. 2021. Evaluating atypical language in autism using automated language measures. *Scientific Reports*, 11(1):10968.

Emanuel A. Schegloff. 2000. Overlapping talk and the organization of turn-taking for conversation. *Language in Society*, 29(1):1–63.

David Wechsler. 2002. WPPSI-III: Wechsler Preschool and Primary Scale of Intelligence - 3rd ed. *San Antonio, TX: Psychological Corporation.*

David Wechsler. 2003. WISC-IV: Wechsler Intelligence Scale for Children. *San Antonio, TX: Psychological Corporation.*

Hans W. Wendt. 1972. Dealing with a common problem in social science: A simplified rank-biserial coefficient of correlation based on the U statistic. *European Journal of Social Psychology*, 2(4):463–465.

A Appendix

See Table 4 ("Demographic and clinical sample characteristics") on page 7.

	ASD *(n = 116, 97 males)*				TD *(n = 65, 37 males)*				
	min	*max*	*mean*	*s.d.*	*min*	*max*	*mean*	*s.d.*	*p*
Age in years	4.54	15.6	10.06	2.81	4.21	14.5	8.22	2.83	<.001
IQ	72	138	102.17	15.81	90	147	116.94	12.37	<.001
ADOS SA	3	19	9.17	3.49	0	8	0.95	1.47	<.001
ADOS RRB	0	8	3.59	1.54	0	2	0.45	0.64	<.001
ADOS Total	7	24	12.76	3.74	0	10	1.40	1.79	<.001
CCC-2 Pragmatic	1.5	10.8	4.96	1.70	7.5	15.8	12.05	1.73	<.001
CCC-2 Structural	1	12	7.01	2.30	8.5	15	11.73	1.57	<.001
CCC-2 GCC	45	103	75.12	11.04	87	143	115.18	12.09	<.001

Table 4: Demographic and clinical sample characteristics. Abbreviations: ADOS = Autism Diagnostic Observation Schedule; SA = Social Affect; RRB = Restricted and Repetitive Behavior; CCC-2 = Children's Communication Checklist, version 2; GCC = Global Communication Composite.

Interactional coordination between conversation partners with autism using non-verbal cues in dialogues

Tahiya Chowdhury, Veronica Romero and **Amanda Stent**
Davis Institute for Artificial Intelligence, Colby College
4000 Mayflower Hill Dr, Waterville, ME 04901
tchowdhu, ajstent, vcromero@colby.edu

Abstract

The diagnosis of autism spectrum disorder (ASD) is a complex, challenging task as it depends on the analysis of dynamic interactional behaviors during diagnostic conversations, including the degree to and ways in which the individual being assessed coordinates their verbal and non-verbal behaviors with their interlocutor (interpersonal coordination), and the degree to which and ways in which they engage in repetitive behaviors (intrapersonal coordination). In this paper, we look at interactional coordination during diagnostic conversations between a psychologist and children who either are typically developing (TD) or have a diagnosis of ASD. Using Cross-Recurrence Quantification Analysis, a method developed for investigating the behavior of dynamic systems, we measure the coordination of non-verbal behaviors between child and psychologist and test whether these measures can be predictive of diagnosis outcome.

1 Introduction

Autism spectrum disorder (ASD) refers to a range of developmental disabilities that affect people's communication, interaction, learning, and other social behaviors. Adolescents with ASD generally exhibit impairments in social interaction (American Psychiatric Organization, 2013), including difficulty in reciprocating verbal and non-verbal behaviors appropriately as well as repetitive behaviors (Tager-Flusberg and Caronna, 2007; Tager-Flusberg, 1999; Mundy and Markus, 1997; Landa, 2000). Previous research on ASD has examined characteristic difficulties in understanding both verbal and non-verbal communication behaviors including following eye gaze (Baron-Cohen et al., 1997), recognizing and imitating gestures (Hobson and Lee, 1999; Williams et al., 2004) and facial expressions (Drimalla et al., 2021), as well as proper use of language pragmatics and verbal reciprocity (Norbury and Bishop, 2002).

A standard diagnostic tool for autism, the Autism Diagnostic Observation Schedule (Lord et al., 2000), relies on qualitative coding by expert assessors for the presence or absence of certain behavioral markers across multiple structured and naturalistic conversational scenarios. The assessor has to simultaneously engage the child in conversation, monitor their own conversational behavior, and make diagnostic notes based on their observations. Understanding the cognitive demands and subjective nature of this process, previous research has explored the efficacy of machine learning methods for identifying behavioral signals of ASD in conversation data (Fusaroli et al., 2019, 2017, 2022). Recent years have seen much more work on computational tools for providing fine-grained, quantitative measurements of conversational behaviors in autism diagnosis conversations. This includes the use of acoustic-prosodic features such as pitch (Kiss et al., 2012), intonation, and rhythm (Bone et al., 2015); language features such as word usage (Song et al., 2021; Prud'hommeaux et al., 2011), discourse expressions (Yang et al., 2021; Chowdhury et al., 2023), social and cognitive linguistic word counts (Kumar et al., 2016), semantic similarity (Goodkind et al., 2018); pose (Kojovic et al., 2021) and mouth movement (Parish-Morris et al., 2018). However, most of this work has examined behaviors either at the individual utterance level, or via conversation-level aggregate statistics. This means that the moment-to-moment dynamic aspects of coordination in conversation are not well captured. Prior work suggests that typically developing children have been shown to spontaneously modify their interaction patterns more than children with ASD to achieve coordination (Marsh et al., 2013; Drimalla et al., 2021). Quantifying interactional coordination under different conversation contexts during autism diagnosis could thus provide insights into an individual's behavioral flexibility to adapt across conversational

Proceedings of the First ICARD Workshop, pages 24–34
September 12, 2023

contexts and its influence on diagnostic outcomes. **Contributions:** First, we introduce recurrence quantification analysis (RQA) and cross-recurrence quantification analysis (CRQA), techniques used in a variety of other fields but almost never used in NLP. RQA and CRQA permit fine-grained modeling of the dynamic systems reflected in one or two time series. Second, we use RQA and CRQA to analyze the dynamic synchronization of non-verbal conversational cues exhibited through the body movements of conversational interlocutors, focusing on conversational diagnostics for autism. We explore the following questions:

- Does interactional coordination evolve differently for typically developing (TD) children and children with ASD?
- Does interactional coordination during autism diagnostic conversations differ by conversational context?
- Can we classify children with ASD and TD children using interactional coordination measures as indicators?

2 Background

Generally speaking, in a conversation or interaction, the interlocutors will coordinate their verbal and non-verbal behaviors (Brennan and Hanna, 2009; Reitter and Moore, 2014; Rasenberg et al., 2020). This dynamic process of coordination is difficult to model or analyze using computational approaches, which generally require fixed-length representations. Traditionally, computational researchers extract summary statistics over the conversation or segments of the conversation (Stenchikova and Stent, 2007; Danescu-Niculescu-Mizil and Lee, 2011; Jones et al., 2014; Dubuisson Duplessis et al., 2021). By contrast, with CRQA it is possible to computationally model the fine-grained patterning of moment-to-moment coordination in conversation.

2.1 Recurrence Quantification Analysis

Recurrence Quantification Analysis (RQA) and Cross-Recurrence Quantification Analysis (CRQA) are non-parametric, non-linear techniques that can be used to analyze any (set of) time series (Zbilut et al., 1998). CRQA has been used by cognitive scientists and psychologists to model the coordination of behaviors by conversational interlocutors (e.g. Dale and Spivey, 2006; Fusaroli et al., 2014; Kodama et al., 2021; Romero and Paxton, 2023), but this technique is so far almost unknown to the NLP community[1].

RQA converts an input time series (with some measure along the y axis and time along the x axis) into a phase-space representation of an estimate of the underlying dynamics of the system that generated it (Webber Jr and Zbilut, 2005). CRQA, an extension of RQA, is used for two time-series (Wallot and Leonardi, 2018). For example, if our only measure of a conversational interlocutor's behavior is the position of their nose (an estimate of directionality of gaze), then our time series would be the x and y coordinates of the positions of each participant's nose over time, but the underlying system would include much more information.

CRQA has been applied to quantify interactions between people in a wide range of modalities. It has been used to quantify heart rate coordination during performances (Konvalinka et al., 2011) and while completing joint construction tasks (Fusaroli et al., 2016). Ramenzoni et al. (2011) found that interpersonal coordination in motor behaviors varies due to the nature of the task performed and can affect individual and joint performance differently. Similarly, Wallot et al. (2016) observed that movement coordination in joint construction tasks depends on the task context, and coordination can affect performance positively or negatively depending on the type of interactions demanded by the task.

CRQA has also been used to explore conversational scenarios to measure the level of coordination through behavior matching in speech, gaze (Richardson and Dale, 2005), and gestures (Louwerse et al., 2012). Shared knowledge between interlocutors that work as a common ground is found to influence coordination achieved during dialogue (Richardson et al., 2007). Richardson et al. (2009) showed that the conversation partner's belief about the contextual information available to the other influences their language usage and coordination. Leonardi (2012) posed conversation as a coordination task where alignment in the form of recurrence can happen in verbal and non-verbal interaction involved, including lexical, syntactic, and movement levels.

[1]We could find only one paper in the ACL Anthology where RQA is used, (Chinaei et al., 2017); other NLP-related papers that use RQA are (Allen et al., 2017; Dale et al., 2018; Song et al., 2023), two of which are unpublished preprints.

The complex dynamics of child language and speech usage in dyadic interaction with adults has been studied using recurrence quantification measures (Cox and van Dijk, 2013) where they found increased dynamic adaptation as the child's language developed with age. Similarly, Dale and Spivey (2006) studied conversations between child and caregiver, and found that the child's ability to coordinate reflects their language acquisition and development. Warlaumont et al. (2010) studied interactional dynamics during conversations between child and caregiver and found recurrent delayed response as an indicator of autism. In a similar study using recurrence analysis, Romero et al. (2016) found differences in interpersonal coordination patterns between children with autism and typically developing across a variety of tasks.

In prior research, several CRQA-based metrics have been used to measure coordination (e.g. Fusaroli et al., 2014; Reuzel et al., 2013; Richardson and Dale, 2005; Louwerse et al., 2012). The ones we used here are:

- **Recurrence Rate (RR)** measures the amount of similarity between the trajectories of the two systems, or the amount of time in which interlocutors showed any kind of interactional coordination during their conversation.
- **Determinism (DET)** measures the determinism or stability of the coordination.
- **Longest Line Length (MaxLine)** is another measure of the stability of the coordination.
- **Entropy (ENTR)** in this context provides a measure of the regularity or irregularity of the coordination over time. Where low ENTR implies regularity of movement and high ENTR means more complex, chaotic movement.
- **Trapping time (TT)** measures the permanence of coordination between the two series.

3 Data

We used video data collected during sessions of the Autism Diagnostic Observation Schedule - Second Edition (ADOS-2), an assessment tool used to categorize ASD (Lord et al., 2000). In this assessment, a child and a certified adult assessor (usually a psychologist) engage in a sequence of semi-structured activities (subtasks). Our data includes fourteen different subtasks from Module 3 of the ADOS-2, which is designed for verbally fluent children and adolescents. Depending on the subtask, the child may be asked to engage in a spontaneous conversation (tell a story, play with toys with the assessor, act out a cartoon, or simply chat) or participate in a structured interview on topics such as social life, friends, or emotions.

Our data involved 29 sessions, each with a different child, administered by a single psychologist assessor. Each session lasted on average 40-60 minutes. 14 children had been previously diagnosed with autism (3 Female) and 15 were age-matched typically developing (TD) children (5 Female) who had not received any diagnosis of a mental disorder in the past. All the children were between the ages of 10 and 15. Those in the ASD group had a mean age of 12.36 years (SD = 1.60) and typically developing children were on average 12.20 years old (SD = 1.93). Of the 14 children with ASD, nine of them were white (no Hispanics) and 5 of them were African American. For the TD group, there were 13 white (2 Hispanics) children, 1 African American child, and 1 Asian child. We split each session recording by subtask using annotations done by a research assistant; the average length of these videos is 5 minutes. We cropped each video into left (child) and right (assessor) participant videos, each of resolution 640x720 pixels. We downsampled the videos to 10 frames per second for efficiency in analysis[2]. We processed the left and right participant videos for each subtask using *OpenPose* (Cao et al., 2017; Cao et al., 2019), obtaining time series of x- and y-coordinates for 25 skeletal keypoints of the person present in the video. In the experiments reported here, we used only four of these key points: nose (head), neck (body), and wrists (hand). This allowed us to capture the temporal dynamics of, and relationships between, the child's and assessor's non-verbal behaviors, without using on-body sensors.

The collection and use of this data were approved by the IRBs at the institutions of the corresponding authors and where the data was collected.

4 Method

In this section, we describe how we fit a CRQA model to our data.

[2]People's movements over time periods of less than 1/10 second are not typically trackable by AI pose tracking software.

Vertical Head Movement

Indicator	F	$p-$value
DET	21.668	< 0.001
TT	6.082	0.05
ENT	21.173	< 0.001
L_{max} (V)	4.918	< 0.05
Delay	84.343	< 0.0001

Horizontal Body Movement

Indicator	F	$p-$value
DET	17.615	< 0.001
TT	14.810	< 0.0001
ENT	37.200	< 0.0001
L_{max} (V)	11.363	< 0.01
Delay	100.395	< 0.0001

Horizontal Hand Movement

Indicator	F	$p-$value
DET	30.069	< 0.0001
TT	20.374	< 0.005
ENT	32.645	< 0.0001
L_{max} (V)	18.810	< 0.005
Delay	78.911	< 0.0001

Vertical Hand Movement

Indicator	F	$p-$value
DET	4.748	< 0.05
TT	1.007	0.3247
ENT	17.712	< 0.001
L_{max} (V)	17.228	< 0.001
Delay	36.080	< 0.0001

Table 1: (Section 5.1) Interpersonal coordination varies between first and last subtasks (results of mixed ANOVA).

4.1 Parameter Selection

For quantifying interactional dynamics between time series pairs of non-verbal conversational behavior, we need to first estimate a set of parameters to reconstruct the phase space dynamics of the time series of interest (Takens, 2006): the embedding dimension m, the delay d, and the radius r.

Delay: The delay d is used to recover the latent dimensions by using embedded copies of the time series at different delays. We estimated delay d using the approach described in prior work (Wallot and Leonardi, 2018). Specifically, we used the delay value at the first local minimum of the average mutual information function (AMI) of the component time-series, since the time-series is most independent of itself at that delay (Abarbanel, 2012).

Embedding dimension: The embedding dimension m is an estimate of the number of latent dimensions responsible for the dynamics. We used the false nearest neighbor (FNN) method (Kennel et al., 1992) to estimate the embedding dimension m. Using the delay parameter to embed the time series, we used the embedding obtained at the first local minimum of FNN.

Radius: The radius r specifies the interval space within which two values are counted as recurrent, as continuous-valued time series usually never repeat at exactly the same value. We chose r by incrementally increasing it until RR reached 4%, which is within the recommended range of 1-5% for behavioral data (Webber Jr and Zbilut, 2005) to balance stochastic and deterministic components of the signal.

As we separately estimated d, m, and r for each analysis, this did not allow us to compare RR across participants and tasks. The dynamics of each conversation were too different to use a fixed set of parameters for all. We used PyRQA (Rawald et al., 2017) for the recurrence analysis and teaspoon (Munch and Khasawneh, 2022) for parameter selection for phase space reconstruction.

We limited our analysis to vertical movement of the head (e.g. nodding), horizontal movement of the body (e.g. postural sway or proximity due to moving closer or apart from the other), and horizontal and vertical movement of hands (gestures), resulting in four pairs of time series of non-verbal cues per conversation. Note that using raw movement as non-verbal behavioral cues is advantageous as it allows us to compare conversations that are seemingly different activity-wise yet involve non-verbal behaviors that are universal to conversations in general.

5 Results

5.1 How does interpersonal coordination change over time and by diagnostic group?

In our first experiment, we examined which movements exhibit greater coordination at the end of ADOS diagnostic conversations vs the beginning. In each of our conversations, participants completed subtasks from Module 3 of ADOS-2 in order; we compared coordination in the last subtask vs the first one. This gave $n = 29$ observations (one pair of subtasks per participant). We used a mixed

Vertical Head Movement

Indicator	Estimates	$p-$value
DET	0.001	0.919
TT	−0.004	0.628
ENT	0.001	0.847
L_{max} (V)	−0.473	0.537
Delay	−3.552	0.082

Horizontal Body Movement

Indicator	Estimates	$p-$value
DET	−0.011	0.429
TT	−0.005	0.548
ENT	0.002	0.843
L_{max} (V)	−2.288	0.278
Delay	−8.679	< 0.01

Horizontal Hand Movement

Indicator	Estimates	$p-$value
DET	−0.004	0.781
TT	−0.003	0.706
ENT	0.004	0.279
L_{max} (V)	−0.530	0.723
Delay	−5.965	< 0.05

Vertical Hand Movement

Indicator	Estimates	$p-$value
DET	−0.007	0.670
TT	0.001	0.934
ENT	0.003	0.668
L_{max} (V)	1.189	0.149
Delay	−2.900	0.204

Table 2: (Section 5.2.1) Interpersonal coordination generally does not vary by diagnostic group (results of linear mixed model).

Vertical Head Movement

Indicator	Estimates	$p-$value
DET	0.002	0.802
TT	0.005	0.532
ENT	0.002	0.708
L_{max} (V)	1.460	< 0.05
Delay	−3.649	< 0.05

Horizontal Body Movement

Indicator	Estimates	$p-$value
DET	0.011	0.443
TT	0.005	0.451
ENT	0.001	0.872
L_{max} (V)	3.225	0.129
Delay	−10.092	< 0.001

Horizontal Hand Movement

Indicator	Estimates	$p-$value
DET	0.013	0.283
TT	−0.010	0.082
ENT	0.003	0.337
L_{max} (V)	2.733	0.051
Delay	−6.942	< 0.005

Vertical Hand Movement

Indicator	Estimates	$p-$value
DET	0.001	0.979
TT	−0.021	< 0.05
ENT	−0.002	0.676
L_{max} (V)	0.788	0.551
Delay	−4.496	< 0.05

Table 3: (Section 5.2.1) Interpersonal coordination varies by subtask type (results of linear mixed model).

2(diagnostic group: TD vs. ASD) x 2(task order: first vs. last) ANOVA for our experiment.

Our results are shown in Table 1. Interpersonal coordination between child and psychologist differs significantly ($p < 0.05$) between the first and last subtask for all modalities, for all metrics other than Trapping Time (which indicates the proportion of time the interlocutors stay in a coordinated state).

For typically developing children, Trapping Time improved between the first task (construction with a puzzle) and the last task (creating a story using props), while for the children with ASD, it remained similar. However, we did not observe a significant difference between the two diagnostic groups for any of the movement modalities, perhaps due to the small number of observations. Prior work on synchronization during joint work made a similar observation: practice and task difficulty improved coordination over time (Louwerse et al., 2012). Here, the subtask type can be considered analogous to task difficulty, so we next look at how coordination changes depending on the subtask type.

5.2 How does interpersonal coordination change with subtask type and diagnostic group?

In our second experiment, we grouped the ADOS-2 module 3 conversation-centric tasks into two types:

Vertical Head Movement

Indicator	Estimates	$p-$value
DET	0.023	< 0.05
TT	0.010	0.059
ENT	0.000	0.829
L_{max} (V)	2.078	< 0.01
Delay	−1.644	0.399

Horizontal Body Movement

Indicator	Estimates	$p-$value
DET	−0.027	0.111
TT	−0.017	0.171
ENT	0.000	0.866
L_{max} (V)	−0.622	0.613
Delay	−6.444	< 0.05

Horizontal Hand Movement

Indicator	Estimates	$p-$value
DET	−0.018	0.439
TT	−0.013	0.454
ENT	0.169	0.909
L_{max} (V)	−0.622	0.613
Delay	−5.563	< 0.05

Vertical Hand Movement

Indicator	Estimates	$p-$value
DET	−0.010	0.576
TT	−0.007	0.650
ENT	0.000	0.872
L_{max} (V)	−0.130	0.917
Delay	−2.051	0.396

Table 4: (Section 5.2.2) Intra-personal coordination generally does not vary by diagnostic group (results of linear mixed model).

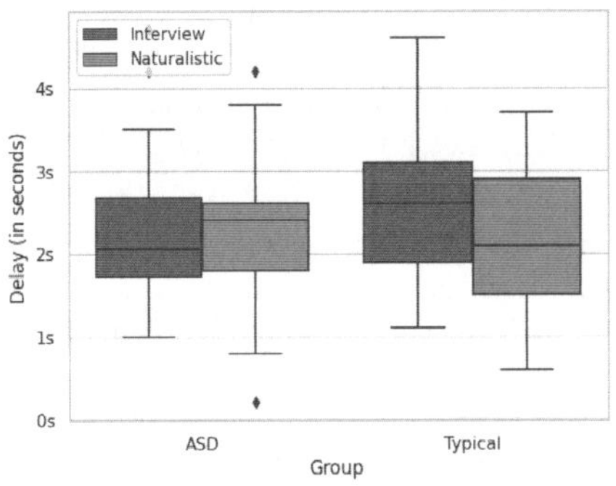

(a) Vertical Head Movement

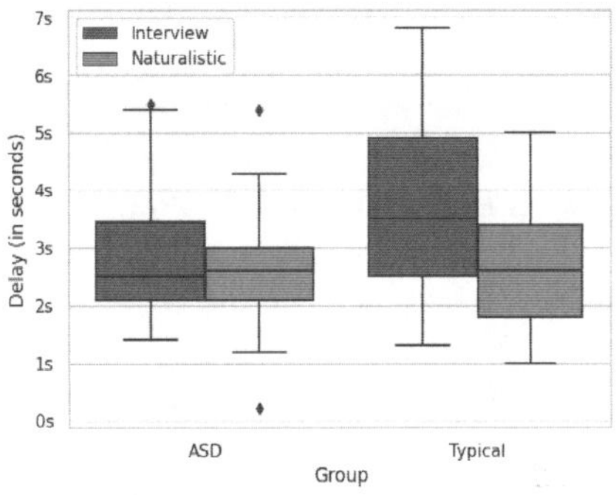

(b) Horizontal Body Movement

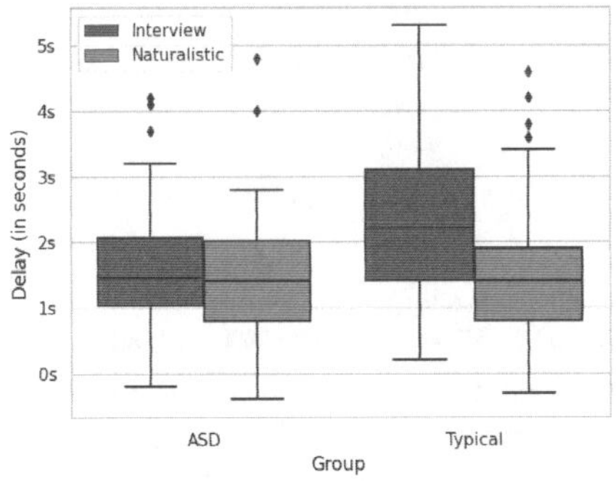

(c) Horizontal Hand Movement

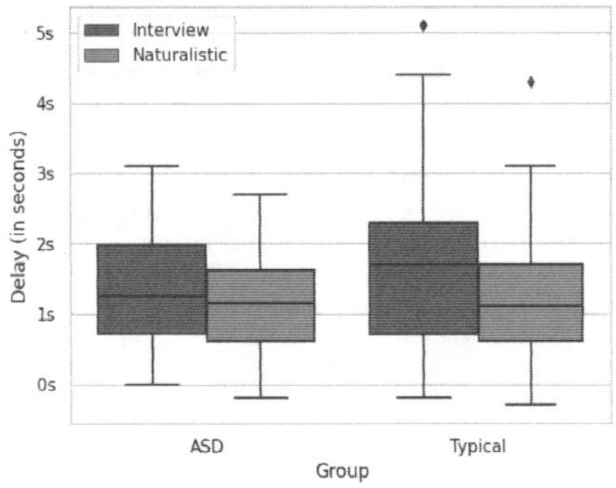

(d) Vertical Hand Movement

Figure 1: Difference in latency for interpersonal coordination in movement

naturalistic and interview. Naturalistic subtasks are those in which the interlocutors engage in unstructured conversations (discussing a picture, talking about a topic of interest, silent play, or unstructured conversation). Interview subtasks are those in which the assessor uses a structured sequence of questions (interviews about social life, friends, or emotions). This gave $n = 169$ observations (three subtasks per participant per subtask type).

Repetitive behavior is a symptom of autism; therefore, we looked at both interpersonal coordination (coordination between interlocutors) us-

Model	Acc.	Prec.	Recall	F1
Naive Bayes	0.48	0.50	0.48	0.40
Decision Tree	0.61	0.68	0.61	0.62
Random Forest	0.62	0.68	0.62	0.63
Adaboost	0.60	0.76	0.60	0.63

Model	Acc.	Prec.	Recall	F1
Naive Bayes	0.30	0.11	0.30	0.15
Decision Tree	0.66	0.72	0.66	0.66
Random Forest	0.61	0.65	0.61	0.61
Adaboost	0.61	0.66	0.61	0.61

Table 5: Classification of autism diagnosis using CRQA metrics of interpersonal coordination (left) and RQA metrics of intrapersonal coordination (right).

ing CRQA, and intrapersonal coordination (self-coordination of the child's behaviors) using RQA. We used linear mixed-effects models with the diagnostic group as the between-group factor and conversation type as the within-group factor.

5.2.1 Interpersonal coordination

Our results are shown in Tables 2 and 3.

Coordination measures decreased or remain nearly unchanged in all 4 behavioral modalities for children with ASD compared to children who are typically developing (Table 2). However, Delay (the latency at which coordination happens) is significantly lower for head movement, hand horizontal movement, and vertical hand movement ($p < 0.05$) in naturalistic subtasks compared to interview subtasks (Table 3). The negative coefficients for all three cases (-3.649, -6.942, -4.496) suggest that children respond more immediately in naturalistic subtasks, perhaps because of the relaxed nature of the conversations. Furthermore, there are significant diagnostic group differences in horizontal body movement and horizontal hand movement for Delay ($p < 0.05$). The negative coefficients for both (-8.679, -5.965) suggest that movement latency is reduced for children with ASD compared to children who are typically developing.

5.2.2 Intrapersonal coordination

Our results are shown in Table 4. We found no significant differences in intrapersonal coordination between naturalistic and interview subtask types. Delay (the latency at which coordination happens) is significantly lower for children with ASD than for children who are typically developing. For vertical head movement (which captures behaviors such as nodding), intrapersonal coordination shows a higher deterministic pattern for children with ASD. This is also evident from Figure 1, which depicts the distribution of coordination delay for the two subtask types between the two diagnostic groups. For children with ASD, in all 4 behavioral modalities, delay either increased or remain unchanged.

5.3 Can information from RQA and CRQA analyses be successfully used in diagnostic classification models?

Recurrence analysis metrics from time series generated from wearable sensors have been used for detecting repetitive motor movement (Großekathöfer et al., 2017). In our third experiment, we used recurrence analysis metrics from time series generated via AI-based human body-skeleton detection in ADOS conversational assessments as features for the classification of autism diagnosis.

As features, we used the same five recurrence analysis metrics as above (DET, TT, ENT, L_{max}, and Delay) obtained from vertical head movement, horizontal body movement, and horizontal and vertical hand movement data from each subtask, plus the task itself, This gave 6 features for each of $n = 1568$ observations (four movements for each of 14 subtasks for each of 29 participating conversational pairs, with 14 subtasks missing because the children declined to participate).

To ensure generalization for out-of-sample testing, we performed cross-validation by using leave-n-user-out [3]. We report results averaged over 10 runs, where 80% (23) of children were randomly selected for training and 20% (6) for testing in each run. We experimented with simple, relatively interpretable classification approaches: Naive Bayes, Decision Tree, Random Forest, and Adaboost[4]. All experiments were run using the scikit-learn and sciPy libraries with default parameter settings. We report accuracy, precision, recall, and F1-score.

We trained one set of models using RQA metrics capturing intrapersonal coordination and another using CRQA metrics capturing interpersonal

[3]We chose this over 10-fold cross-validation, as this ensures our training set does not include information from a child who is also present in our test set.

[4]Our goal in this work is to give assessors *assessment support tools*, not to support automated diagnosis. For this reason, the interpretability of model decisions is important. In addition to the results presented here, we tried multi-layer perceptrons and support vector machines, which performed worse than a random baseline.

coordination. Our results are shown in Table 5. Decision trees were the best-performing approach with RQA across all metrics; tree-based models (Adaboost, Random Forests, and decision trees) performed similarly with CRQA metrics. In both cases, Naive Bayes performs worse than a random baseline; this can be attributed to its strong feature independence assumption. No modeling approach gave results good enough likely to make it a useful assessment support tool for ADOS assessors; however, it is possible that by combining CRQA or RQA-derived features with acoustic/prosodic and language-derived features, we could obtain better results (see Chowdhury et al., 2023).

6 Limitations

We would like to emphasize that this study is preliminary. The sample set is relatively small, and the number of non-verbal behaviors we had the opportunity to evaluate is also relatively small.

In addition, although our results and those of others cited in this paper show that automated measures extracted from autism assessments may be somewhat predictive of autism diagnosis, we *in no way* mean to imply that it is now or will soon be possible (or even desirable) to automate autism diagnosis. Especially since the tools available to us at the moment, like *OpenPose* need to be improved to consistently extract movement data from video (Chung et al., 2022). We would like to drive this point home:

- There is an element of subjectivity in manual assessment diagnosis of autism; yet, all the diagnosis data that we have comes from these manual assessments. This means the labels are noisy.

- There are demographic limitations in the available data. The relatively small amount of data available from manual assessments for autism is not balanced for important factors including sex, gender, ethnicity, race, country of origin, language, age, educational status, or income status. This means the data is biased.

- Given these concerns, and the growing literature on biased outcomes of automated assessments for marginalized populations, it is our position that *any decision* involving a significant outcome for a human being should have a human involved.

Our long-term goal is therefore not to provide a machine learning-based "autism test", but to provide machine learning-based automatic measures that an assessor can use to examine the acceptability of assessment sessions and to inform their own diagnostic decisions.

7 Conclusions and Future Work

In this work, we explore a method for quantifying interactional coordination in autism assessment. We use non-verbal movement exhibited through head, body, and hand positions to capture movement dynamics during conversation and measure coordination over time. We show that coordination between interlocutors changes over time for both children who are typically developing and children who exhibit symptoms of ASD.

Importantly, we find that the level and stability (as measured by L_{max} and TT) of both inter-and intra-personal coordination do not generally differ by diagnostic group. We also find that coordination delay was significantly lower for the ASD group in both interpersonal and intra-personal coordination, which conforms to the existing literature on response delay as a symptom of autism. Interestingly, this finding does provide some insight into how children in each diagnostic group exhibit different dynamics, even though these differences were not captured by ENT. Contextual information such as subtask type (interview vs. naturalistic) does influence the degree of coordination between the interlocutors, but does not affect the child's coordination within their own behavior.

In future research, we plan to extend our analysis to other interactional behaviors including non-verbal cues such as facial expressions, eye gaze and verbal cues such as acoustic-prosodic behaviors (pitch, intonation), word usage, and discourse usage for measuring interpersonal and intra-personal coordination during diagnostic conversations.

8 Acknowledgements

We would like to thank and acknowledge all our participants and their families. The data set was obtained thanks to support from the National Institute of Mental Health and the National Institutes of Health: awards R21MH094659 and F31MH108331.

References

Henry Abarbanel. 2012. *Analysis of observed chaotic data*. Springer Science & Business Media.

Laura K Allen, Aaron D Likens, and Danielle McNamara. 2017. Recurrence quantification analysis: A technique for the dynamical analysis of student writing. In *Proceedings of the International Florida Artificial Intelligence Research Society Conference (FLAIRS)*, pages 240–245.

American Psychiatric Organization. 2013. *Diagnostic and statistical manual of mental disorders (DSM-5)*. American Psychiatric Publishing, Washington, DC.

Simon Baron-Cohen, Sally Wheelwright, , and Therese Jolliffe. 1997. Is there a "language of the eyes"? evidence from normal adults, and adults with autism or asperger syndrome. *Visual Cognition*, 4(3):311–331.

Daniel Bone, Matthew P Black, Anil Ramakrishna, Ruth B Grossman, and Shrikanth S Narayanan. 2015. Acoustic-prosodic correlates of 'awkward'prosody in story retellings from adolescents with autism. In *Proceedings of INTERSPEECH*, pages 1616–1620.

Susan E Brennan and Joy E Hanna. 2009. Partner-specific adaptation in dialog. *Topics in Cognitive Science*, 1(2):274–291.

Z. Cao, G. Hidalgo Martinez, T. Simon, S. Wei, and Y. A. Sheikh. 2019. Openpose: Realtime multi-person 2d pose estimation using part affinity fields. *IEEE Transactions on Pattern Analysis and Machine Intelligence*.

Zhe Cao, Tomas Simon, Shih-En Wei, and Yaser Sheikh. 2017. Realtime multi-person 2d pose estimation using part affinity fields. In *Proceedings of CVPR*.

Hamidreza Chinaei, Leila Chan Currie, Andrew Danks, Hubert Lin, Tejas Mehta, and Frank Rudzicz. 2017. Identifying and avoiding confusion in dialogue with people with alzheimer's disease. *Computational Linguistics*, 43(2):377–406.

Tahiya Chowdhury, Veronica Romero, and Amanda Stent. 2023. Parameter selection for analyzing conversations with autism spectrum disorder. In *Proceedings of INTERSPEECH*.

Jen-Li Chung, Lee-Yeng Ong, and Meng-Chew Leow. 2022. Comparative analysis of skeleton-based human pose estimation. *Future Internet*, 14(12).

Ralf F. A. Cox and Marijn van Dijk. 2013. Microdevelopment in parent-child conversations: From global changes to flexibility. *Ecological Psychology*, 25(3):304–315.

Rick Dale, Nicholas D Duran, and Moreno Coco. 2018. Dynamic natural language processing with recurrence quantification analysis. *arXiv preprint arXiv:1803.07136*.

Rick Dale and Michael J Spivey. 2006. Unraveling the dyad: Using recurrence analysis to explore patterns of syntactic coordination between children and caregivers in conversation. *Language Learning*, 56(3):391–430.

Cristian Danescu-Niculescu-Mizil and Lillian Lee. 2011. Chameleons in imagined conversations: A new approach to understanding coordination of linguistic style in dialogs. In *Proceedings of the 2nd Workshop on Cognitive Modeling and Computational Linguistics*, pages 76–87.

Hanna Drimalla, Irina Baskow, Behnoush Behnia, Stefan Roepke, and Isabel Dziobek. 2021. Imitation and recognition of facial emotions in autism: a computer vision approach. *Molecular Autism*, 12:1–15.

Guillaume Dubuisson Duplessis, Caroline Langlet, Chloé Clavel, and Frédéric Landragin. 2021. Towards alignment strategies in human-agent interactions based on measures of lexical repetitions. *Language Resources and Evaluation*, 55:353–388.

Riccardo Fusaroli, Johanne S Bjørndahl, Andreas Roepstorff, and Kristian Tylén. 2016. A heart for interaction: Shared physiological dynamics and behavioral coordination in a collective, creative construction task. *Journal of Experimental Psychology: Human Perception and Performance*, 42(9):1297.

Riccardo Fusaroli, Ruth Grossman, Niels Bilenberg, Cathriona Cantio, Jens Richardt Møllegaard Jepsen, and Ethan Weed. 2022. Toward a cumulative science of vocal markers of autism: A cross-linguistic meta-analysis-based investigation of acoustic markers in American and Danish autistic children. *Autism Research: Official Journal of the International Society for Autism Research*, 15(4):653–664.

Riccardo Fusaroli, Ivana Konvalinka, and Sebastian Wallot. 2014. Analyzing social interactions: the promises and challenges of using cross recurrence quantification analysis. In *Translational recurrences: From mathematical theory to real-world applications*, pages 137–155. Springer.

Riccardo Fusaroli, Anna Lambrechts, Dan Bang, Dermot M Bowler, and Sebastian B Gaigg. 2017. Is voice a marker for autism spectrum disorder? a systematic review and meta-analysis. *Autism Research: Official Journal of the International Society for Autism Research*, 10(3):384–407.

Riccardo Fusaroli, Ethan Weed, Deborah Fein, and Letitia Naigles. 2019. Hearing me hearing you: Reciprocal effects between child and parent language in autism and typical development. *Cognition*, 183:1–18.

Adam Goodkind, Michelle Lee, Gary E Martin, Molly Losh, and Klinton Bicknell. 2018. Detecting language impairments in autism: A computational analysis of semi-structured conversations with vector semantics. In *Proceedings of the Society for Computation in Linguistics (SCiL) 2018*, pages 12–22.

Ulf Großekathöfer, Nikolay V Manyakov, Vojkan Mihajlović, Gahan Pandina, Andrew Skalkin, Seth Ness, Abigail Bangerter, and Matthew S Goodwin. 2017. Automated detection of stereotypical motor movements in autism spectrum disorder using recurrence quantification analysis. *Frontiers in neuroinformatics*, 11:9.

R Peter Hobson and Anthony Lee. 1999. Imitation and identification in autism. *The Journal of Child Psychology and Psychiatry and Allied Disciplines*, 40(4):649–659.

Simon L Jones, Rachel Cotterill, Nigel Dewdney, Kate Muir, and Adam N Joinson. 2014. Finding zelig in text: A measure for normalising linguistic accommodation. In *Proceedings of COLING*.

Matthew B Kennel, Reggie Brown, and Henry DI Abarbanel. 1992. Determining embedding dimension for phase-space reconstruction using a geometrical construction. *Physical review A*, 45(6):3403.

Géza Kiss, Jan PH van Santen, Emily Prud'Hommeaux, and Lois M Black. 2012. Quantitative analysis of pitch in speech of children with neurodevelopmental disorders. In *Proceedings of INTERSPEECH*.

Kentaro Kodama, Daichi Shimizu, Rick Dale, and Kazuki Sekine. 2021. An approach to aligning categorical and continuous time series for studying the dynamics of complex human behavior. *Frontiers in Psychology*, 12:614431.

Nada Kojovic, Shreyasvi Natraj, Sharada Prasanna Mohanty, Thomas Maillart, and Marie Schaer. 2021. Using 2d video-based pose estimation for automated prediction of autism spectrum disorders in young children. *Scientific Reports*, 11(1):1–10.

Ivana Konvalinka, Dimitris Xygalatas, Joseph Bulbulia, Uffe Schjødt, Else-Marie Jegindø, Sebastian Wallot, Guy Van Orden, and Andreas Roepstorff. 2011. Synchronized arousal between performers and related spectators in a fire-walking ritual. *Proceedings of the National Academy of Sciences*, 108(20):8514–8519.

Manoj Kumar, Rahul Gupta, Daniel Bone, Nikolaos Malandrakis, Somer Bishop, and Shrikanth S. Narayanan. 2016. Objective Language Feature Analysis in Children with Neurodevelopmental Disorders During Autism Assessment. In *Proceedings of INTERSPEECH*, pages 2721–2725.

Rebecca Landa. 2000. Social language use in Asperger syndrome and high-functioning autism. In *Asperger Syndrome*, pages 125–155. The Guilford Press, New York, NY, US.

Giuseppe Leonardi. 2012. The study of language and conversation with recurrence analysis methods. *Psychology of Language and Communication*, 16(2):165–183.

Catherine Lord, Susan Risi, Linda Lambrecht, Edwin H. Cook, Bennett L. Leventhal, Pamela C. DiLavore, Andrew Pickles, and Michael Rutter. 2000. The Autism diagnostic observation schedule—generic: A standard measure of social and communication deficits associated with the spectrum of Autism. *Journal of Autism and Developmental Disorders*, 30(3):205–223.

Max M Louwerse, Rick Dale, Ellen G Bard, and Patrick Jeuniaux. 2012. Behavior matching in multimodal communication is synchronized. *Cognitive science*, 36(8):1404–1426.

L. Marsh, A. Pearson, D. Ropar, and A. Hamilton. 2013. Children with autism do not overimitate. *Current Biology*, 23(7):R266–R268.

Elizabeth Munch and Firas Khasawneh. 2022. teaspoon.

Peter Mundy and Jessica Markus. 1997. On the nature of communication and language impairment in autism. *Mental Retardation and Developmental Disabilities Research Reviews*, 3(4):343–349.

Courtenay Frazier Norbury and Dorothy VM Bishop. 2002. Inferential processing and story recall in children with communication problems: a comparison of specific language impairment, pragmatic language impairment and high-functioning autism. *International Journal of Language & Communication Disorders*, 37(3):227–251.

Julia Parish-Morris, Evangelos Sariyanidi, Casey Zampella, G. Keith Bartley, Emily Ferguson, Ashley A. Pallathra, Leila Bateman, Samantha Plate, Meredith Cola, Juhi Pandey, Edward S. Brodkin, Robert T. Schultz, and Birkan Tunç. 2018. Oral-motor and lexical diversity during naturalistic conversations in adults with autism spectrum disorder. In *Proceedings of the Fifth Workshop on Computational Linguistics and Clinical Psychology: From Keyboard to Clinic*.

Emily T. Prud'hommeaux, Brian Roark, Lois M. Black, and Jan van Santen. 2011. Classification of atypical language in autism. In *Proceedings of the 2nd Workshop on Cognitive Modeling and Computational Linguistics*, pages 88–96.

Verónica C Ramenzoni, Tehran J Davis, Michael A Riley, Kevin Shockley, and Aimee A Baker. 2011. Joint action in a cooperative precision task: nested processes of intrapersonal and interpersonal coordination. *Experimental Brain Research*, 211:447–457.

Marlou Rasenberg, Asli Özyürek, and Mark Dingemanse. 2020. Alignment in multimodal interaction: An integrative framework. *Cognitive Science*, 44(11):e12911.

Tobias Rawald, Mike Sips, and Norbert Marwan. 2017. Pyrqa—conducting recurrence quantification analysis on very long time series efficiently. *Computers and Geosciences*, 104:101–108.

David Reitter and Johanna D Moore. 2014. Alignment and task success in spoken dialogue. *Journal of Memory and Language*, 76:29–46.

Ellen Reuzel, Petri JCM Embregts, Anna MT Bosman, Ralf Cox, Maroesjka van Nieuwenhuijzen, and Andrew Jahoda. 2013. Conversational synchronization in naturally occurring settings: A recurrence-based analysis of gaze directions and speech rhythms of staff and clients with intellectual disability. *Journal of Nonverbal Behavior*, 37:281–305.

Daniel C Richardson and Rick Dale. 2005. Looking to understand: The coupling between speakers' and listeners' eye movements and its relationship to discourse comprehension. *Cognitive science*, 29(6):1045–1060.

Daniel C Richardson, Rick Dale, and Natasha Z Kirkham. 2007. The art of conversation is coordination. *Psychological Science*, 18(5):407–413.

Daniel C Richardson, Rick Dale, and John M Tomlinson. 2009. Conversation, gaze coordination, and beliefs about visual context. *Cognitive Science*, 33(8):1468–1482.

Veronica Romero, Paula Fitzpatrick, RC Schmidt, and Michael J Richardson. 2016. Using cross-recurrence quantification analysis to understand social motor coordination in children with autism spectrum disorder. In *Recurrence Plots and Their Quantifications: Expanding Horizons: Proceedings of the 6th International Symposium on Recurrence Plots*, pages 227–240. Springer.

Veronica Romero and Alexandra Paxton. 2023. Stage 2: Visual information and communication context as modulators of interpersonal coordination in face-to-face and videoconference-based interactions. *Acta Psychologica*, 239:103992.

Amber Song, Meredith Cola, Samantha Plate, Victoria Petrulla, Lisa Yankowitz, Juhi Pandey, Robert T Schultz, and Julia Parish-Morris. 2021. Natural language markers of social phenotype in girls with autism. *Journal of Child Psychology and Psychiatry*, 62(8):949–960.

Yukyeong Song, Wanli Xing, Xiaoyi Tian, and Chenglu Li. 2023. Are we on the same page? modeling linguistic synchrony and math literacy in mathematical discussions.

Svetlana Stenchikova and Amanda Stent. 2007. Measuring adaptation between dialogs. In *Proceedings of the 8th SIGdial Workshop on Discourse and Dialogue*, pages 166–173.

Helen Tager-Flusberg. 1999. A psychological approach to understanding the social and language impairments in autism. *International Review of Psychiatry*, 11(4):325–334.

Helen Tager-Flusberg and Elizabeth Caronna. 2007. Language disorders: Autism and other pervasive developmental disorders. *Pediatric Clinics of North America*, 54(3):469–481.

Floris Takens. 2006. Detecting strange attractors in turbulence. In *Dynamical Systems and Turbulence, Warwick 1980: proceedings of a symposium held at the University of Warwick 1979/80*, pages 366–381. Springer.

Sebastian Wallot and Giuseppe Leonardi. 2018. Analyzing multivariate dynamics using cross-recurrence quantification analysis (CRQA), diagonal-cross-recurrence profiles (DCRP), and multidimensional recurrence quantification analysis (MdRQA) – a tutorial in R. *Frontiers in Psychology*, 9.

Sebastian Wallot, Panagiotis Mitkidis, John J McGraw, and Andreas Roepstorff. 2016. Beyond synchrony: joint action in a complex production task reveals beneficial effects of decreased interpersonal synchrony. *PloS One*, 11(12):e0168306.

Anne S Warlaumont, D Kimbrough Oller, Rick Dale, Jeffrey A Richards, Jill Gilkerson, and Dongxin Xu. 2010. Vocal interaction dynamics of children with and without autism. In *Proceedings of the Annual Meeting of the Cognitive Science Society*, volume 32.

Charles L Webber Jr and Joseph P Zbilut. 2005. Recurrence quantification analysis of nonlinear dynamical systems. *Tutorials in contemporary nonlinear methods for the behavioral sciences*, 94(2005):26–94.

Justin HG Williams, Andrew Whiten, and Tulika Singh. 2004. A systematic review of action imitation in autistic spectrum disorder. *Journal of autism and developmental disorders*, 34:285–299.

Christine Yang, Duanchen Liu, Qingyun Yang, Zoey Liu, and Emily Prud'hommeaux. 2021. Predicting pragmatic discourse features in the language of adults with autism spectrum disorder. In *Proceedings of the 59th Annual Meeting of the Association for Computational Linguistics and the 11th International Joint Conference on Natural Language Processing: Student Research Workshop*, pages 284–291, Online. Association for Computational Linguistics.

Joseph P Zbilut, Alessandro Giuliani, and Charles L Webber Jr. 1998. Detecting deterministic signals in exceptionally noisy environments using cross-recurrence quantification. *Physics Letters A*, 246(1-2):122–128.

AUTHOR INDEX